HEAVY HORSES

AN ANTHOLOGY

EDWARD HART

ALAN SUTTON PUBLISHING LIMITED

First published in the United Kingdom in 1994
Alan Sutton Publishing Limited
Phoenix Mill · Far Thrupp · Stroud · Gloucestershire

First published in the United States of America in 1994
Alan Sutton Publishing Inc.
83 Washington Street · Dover · NH 03820

British Library Cataloguing-in-Publication Data

A catalogue record for this book is available from the British Library.

ISBN 0–7509–0414–3

Library of Congress Cataloging-in-Publication Data applied for

Typeset in 10/13 Sabon
Typesetting and origination by
Alan Sutton Publishing Limited.
Printed in Great Britain by
Butler and Tanner, Frome, Somerset.

Contents

A Clydesdale Unicorn at the 1992 Royal Highland Show. Hugh Ramsey is driving. (Audrey Hart)

Introduction

An alternative word for 'anthology' in Roget's *Thesaurus* is 'treasury'. That exactly describes this book. It is a selection of the best writings on the heavy horse since it began its widespread role, and even before that if we include the work of the agricultural writer and poet Thomas Tusser. In his sixteenth-century day, work horses were smaller and less powerful, yet along with oxen provided motive power for the land.

'Cart horse' is an alternative term for the 'heavy horse'. It is sometimes used derogatively, symbolizing something slow, plodding and ponderous. The best heavy horses were never that, and the modern version, as it circles the show ring at a spanking trot, is the epitome of graceful strength in motion.

The Shire Horse Society began life as the English Cart-Horse Society, 1878, and so continued for the first five volumes of its stud book until 1885. As the most widespread of the heavy breeds, the Shire is sometimes regarded as a synonym for 'heavy'. Vendors of calendars recognize the name's universal appeal, but the Shire horse is but one of four heavy breeds, the others being Clydesdale, Percheron and Suffolk. The more recently imported Ardennes is now staking a claim. The Belgian is widely found in North America, and may become more popular in Britain, but that, perhaps, is for the future.

There was a plethora of writings on carriage, coach, hunting and racehorses from the late eighteenth century onwards. Their owners were comparatively wealthy people, with enough education to enable them to read books on their favourite subjects. Writers and publishers naturally catered for them. The working farmer, the city stable proprietor, the farmworker and the ostler were less able to buy and read books, so we turn to writings on veterinary science and farm management for early references.

In this anthology is traced the rise of the heavy draught horse from the days when it competed with and then took over from oxen. By 1914 there were almost one and a half million horses on farms in Great Britain. The zenith in pedigree numbers came after the First World War, when the 1919, 1920 and 1921 *Clydesdale Stud Books* contained new registrations of 700 stallions and 5,000 mares in their combined width of nearly seven inches! Agricultural depression between the wars was so severe that there was no scope for development; the same old implements continued to be used. Agricultural statistics show that horse numbers had almost halved by 1934, and town use decreased quicker still. The great slaughter of heavy horses during the late 1940s and early 1950s had one benefit; only the best were retained, and so the few remaining thousands were usually of kind temperament.

From near extinction – the Suffolk Horse Society at one time estimated that it could survive only another five years – there has been a revival so great that no one gaining hope in the early 1970s would have dared to predict it. The East of England Show in 1994 sported five 'sixes', ten four-horse teams, twelve Unicorns, twenty-five Pairs and over twenty Singles. There was a strong Agricultural class, Single and Pair Obstacle Driving for light relief, not to mention the breed classes for Shire, Clydesdale, Suffolk and Percheron.

A German branch of the Shire Horse Society has been formed. American Thomas Smrt keeps 500 Shires at Fox Valley Farms, Marengo, Illinois, and donated a team of six black Shires to the United States government for ceremonial use, for which purpose they are ideal. HM The Queen has chosen coloured Clydesdales or big piebalds and skewbalds to present to some of her regiments as drum horses. Leading breweries seek massive horses for advertising-cum-delivery purposes.

These uses are but the spearhead of a movement permeating down the ranks. To own and show a heavy horse has become a popular hobby among those formerly engaged in active and sometimes dangerous sports. Several turnout drivers were once racing motor cyclists; others have turned from rugby and other active games to the fascination of keeping a Shire or Suffolk in stable and paddock. Though the former is the more widespread, Suffolks retain a stronghold in their native East Anglia and have spread into Wales and the West Country. Devon and Dorset banks are safer to work with a team than a tractor.

A generation has grown up for whom the sight of a working horse in a city street is a novelty. This interest has been tapped by a proliferation of heavy horse centres, which extend to rare breed parks showing sheep, cattle, pigs and poultry to a mainly urban clientele, and do nothing but good. This book will appeal to them as much as to the dwindling band to whom my *Golden Guinea Book of Heavy Horse Past and Present* was dedicated in 1976: 'To those who kept the heavy horse flag flying, when all seemed lost'.

Tribute must be paid to the skilled photographers who have posed Shire or Clydesdale to perfection, and captured in sepia or black and white those finer details so beloved of the horse student. G.H. Parsons was among the first and best. His *Types of Modern Shire* (1909) is an invaluable record of the breed during its 'feathery' days, and to turn the large pages is to realize why people brought up in that era class modern fine, silky hair as 'not belonging to real

Shires'. The pencil illustrations of Duvall in Volume I of *The Suffolk Stud Book* are perfection, alluded to in the chapter on that breed.

Poets have been inspired more by the draught horse's efforts than by its looks. Edward Thomas captured the somnolence of Sunday afternoons long ago with his 'three cart-horses looking over a gate, drowsily through their forelocks . . .'.

In the second half of the twentieth century men who had spent their formative years on farms recalled their early days. Incessant horse talk is embalmed in their poetry and prose; several wrote only one book, but these have been sought out and extracts quoted.

Lucy Kemp-Welch, whose painting adorns the jacket of this book, was one artist who loved to capture on canvas the muscular effort of the working horse. Painters like George Stubbs (1724–1806) really understood anatomy, as would be expected of a powerful man reputed to have carried a horse up two flights of stairs to his dissecting-room unaided!

Another was J.F. Herring, examples of whose work are included. Walter Shaw Sparrow in *British Sporting Artists* tells us: 'Herring's fondness for blacksmiths and their forges lasted from his earliest boyhood to 1865, the year of his death.'

Heavy horses are a year-round activity. The first major show of the season is staged at Peterborough in March, and is termed 'The Spring Show' by its Shire followers. Next is the Clydesdale's stallion show. Early in May comes the Percheron's own fixture, with the Suffolks later that month. From then right into September there are heavy horse classes at the Royal and the main county shows, and in town or village events throughout the land.

In September the foal sales start. Here is a chance to pick next year's winners, and to see the stamp of foal left by the various stallions. October brings more sales and ploughing matches, a form of heavy horse sport with its own band of devotees. Far from the bustle of summer shows, these matches in mist or hazy sunshine are on picturesque sites, and gain more entrants each year. The skill is the apex of the horseman's art, and though he may never replace tractor power, the competent ploughman can do any other job that arises with horses.

Wembley's Shire Horse of the Year championship in October is a crown battled for since the first qualifying round in March. There are more foal sales, but the turnout grooms thankfully put away their harness in the knowledge that it will not need cleaning again for some time. They do not remain idle. Ribbons and wool and floral decorations need checking or replacing, new items being chosen from Terry Keegan's invaluable store. The horses themselves are turned away to wide, sheltered pasture or barn, with no need for peak performance next day.

The author, Edward Hart (left), chatting to Shire breeder Denys Benson. Wembley's Musical Drive horses form the background.

Winter evenings are ideal for classifying old catalogues, planning next year's show or work season, and reading anything from the old stud books to the excellent range of literature now available on the heavy horse. If this volume gives pleasure in itself and opens new doors, it will have served its purpose.

Edward Hart
July 1994

one

Early Experiences

Almost half a century has passed since the disappearance of the heavy horse from the land following the Second World War, when a whole way of life seemed to vanish with them. Men who were then youths carried their memories with them, and more recently have had their recollections published. The result is a number of excellent books from the ample raw material on hand. This section makes a selection from that fascinating store.

Often the memories of those young farm-hands included corn harvest. Thomas Hood (1799–1845) wrote

> Oh, there's nothing in life like making love,
> Save making hay in fine weather.

Horsemen generally preferred harvest to haytime; there was less of a mad rush, and less chance of devastating showers. In a fine and settled time, carts and wagons creaked readily over hard ground, short stubble polished one's boots and swished musically with every step, horses strained and then rested, halting between each pair of stooks and again at the stackside. Theirs was not the unceasing work of ploughing but a less strenuous stop-start. And in the warm dusk, few tasks were more fulfilling than stripping off the harnesses, giving a quick rub down, and leading the horses through the gate to watch them flick their heels and enjoy their hard-earned freedom.

Town carters were equally fond of their charges, and confronted problems unimagined by their country counterparts. But the ceaseless processions of horses of all types never palled as a modern traffic queue so quickly does. My predecessor on *Horse and Hound*, Andy Wyndham-Brown, was born around the turn of the century, but always said that he was just too late for the peak of the horse age.

The Decline and the Fall and the Rise of the Horse

The *Decline and fall of the horse* would have made a good book title. Fortunately nobody wrote it. Now it's too late. For the horse has risen again.

Having lived through the final years of the Decline and stayed on to witness the Renaissance, I have been asked for a few memories. It may be hard for the young to realize just how much the horse was a part of almost every life even half a century ago. It tilled the soil, delivered the bread, the milk, the coal. Even the underground miner worked with it.

My earliest memories are as clear about horses as about people. There was my family, there were farm workers who seemed like an extension of it, and there were horses.

Among the men was Jack Banyard, later to be followed by his son 'Young Jack' who was a territorial Green Howard with me at the start of the Second World War. There was 'Old Billy' Atkinson who believed himself to have been one of the last men on the treadmill at York City Castle. They were horsemen. They had tremendous character and I am glad to have been born in time to know them.

Among the horses were two Shires, Boxer and Stella, who were so inseparable that when Stella died Boxer was inconsolable and almost wasted away. There was Daisy who looked a bit like a Clydesdale but not quite and

The Old Grey Horse, by George Morland (1763–1804). Horses are usually painted at the height of their pomp, and this is a splendid example of a thin-fleshed old stager with placid eye. Her hurrying days are over. (Sally Mitchell Prints)

was of a type that I later learned was called a vanner. She had been an army horse in the recently concluded First World War and my father referred to her as a war horse. I remember regarding her with respect and thinking what memories she must have.

When Stella died and the sad, rapidly wasting Boxer hung around the building where he had last seen her, a neighbour's boar pig took to coming on the farm and attacking the horses. They were terrified of him as he charged, apparently attempting to slit their bellies. They ran, making no attempt at defence.

About this time my father and his brother found a replacement for Stella. His name was Butler and he was imposing, even for a Shire. He must have stood 19 hh with beautiful feathering and enormous feet. On the walk to the farm he was taken to the blacksmith's and reshod. With thick, heavy steel on those great hooves he was formidable. But he was restrained and gentle – except when roused.

This happened only once.

He was turned out with the other horses and there was not the usual kicking. He just settled straight in. The herd order and his supremacy must have been apparent and without question.

Soon after his arrival the boar came over and charged toward Boxer who ran, terrified, to the far end of the field.

So the pig turned its attention to the new arrival. Butler took no notice of it until it was within range of his near-hind hoof, then gave it a gentle fly-kick. The boar circled round and came in from the other side.

Then the human audience leaning over the stack-yard gate saw Butler, still grazing, repeat his warning kick with his off-hind.

The boar, now enraged, backed off, circled round and charged as one supposes a rhino might – with enormous speed and terrifying weight.

Butler seemed to consider that things had gone far enough. At exactly the right moment, at precisely the right distance, he caught the pig with both his newly-shod back feet. It was some time before the pig got up. He never came again.

On the edge of the provision market were the covered carriers' carts with their empty shafts, horses and drivers having gone to one of the pubs which were open all day on 'market days and fair days'. You would hear the tradesmen in their shops telling their errand boys to take a parcel to 'the Marton carrier' or 'the Slingsby carrier' who were important links for passengers and goods between their villages and the town.

Back on the farms mechanization was just about to transfer men from the fields to the dole. But apart from its 'waste' of manpower, field operations were very efficient. Haymaking was building weather-proof 'pikes' containing about half a ton of hay. A couple of trace chains were drawn round them and they were hauled to the stack. Also on the go was a horse-drawn sweep. The hay was hoisted to stack level by a pole and pulley device powered by a pony. My job was to do the horse-raking with the pony and then transfer the pony to the elevating operation. We got some good hay and beat some bad weather.

The bigger farms had specialist wagoners but even general farm workers could all handle horses and some took a great pride in their turnout.

The stable was the social centre on the bigger farms where men, engaged for the year, would meet in the evenings to the light of stable or hurricane lamps. Mouth organs and the game of Merelles (or Nine Men Morris) were the entertainment – the Merelles boards were carved on the wooden corn-bin tops.

Most farm men could ride after a fashion. It never occurred to them (or me) that lessons were required. And riding saddles were a rarity.

The Second World War speeded mechanization both in agriculture and the army. I met many regular soldiers who had joined up and served in such places as the North-West Frontier (if there are any other such places) as drivers of horse-drawn guns. They were being retrained. The territorial yeomanry

How they differ. Miles' *Modern Practical Farriery* (1890s), shows the proportions of the darker shaded draught horse, against those of the Thoroughbred.

regiments were called up with their horses. Our Yorkshire Hussars got as far as Palestine before being mechanized.

In Belgium in 1940 I was with another two soldiers when we were told the Belgians had capitulated. Though recent economic events have now made many Britons familiar with the term, it was virtually unknown to us in those days and we were not quite sure what it meant. Round the corner it was quite apparent. A Belgian artillery outfit was breaking its guns and turning its horses loose. Some survived. Many died in fear.

This was perhaps the lowest and saddest point in the Decline of the Horse.

But, unknown at the time, a shipload of cavalry remounts from America was coming up the Channel for the French army. France being overrun by the enemy, the horses were deflected to England.

One of them was a Texas cob called Sweep. He and I were to meet later – when the war was over. Together we took part in the Great Renaissance.

ALAN EXLEY, *HEAVY HORSE & DRIVING*, 1977

The End of an Era

It was early in May 1939 and the sun was shining brightly as I walked along the road from Britwell to Cocksherd Meadow, passing the orchards rich with blossom and the buzz of bees, the latter as yet safe from sprays and man's destruction. The rhythmic clip-clop of the horses' hooves on the hard road gave a sense of peace and security. It was a Saturday. The cart horses were to be turned out to grass for the weekend, the first time that spring. There were four of us escorting the eight massive Suffolk Punches. It did not require that number, except possibly to release them for their first mad gallop after months of restriction; we just wanted to watch when they gained their freedom. I led Boxer and Sprey, rich dark chestnuts in magnificent condition, their coats glistening in the hot sunlight. Both were well over three-quarters of a ton of well-muscled power and yet both were as gentle as kittens.

The estate lorry passed, Harry Jaycock, the driver, giving us a cheery wave. Boxer snorted and pulled away, eyes rolling, showing fear as well he might. It was barely eighteen months since he had been hit by a lorry. It had come down the hill from the direction of Leas Farm towards Cocksherd Wood, and the brakes had failed. Jim Brookling, returning from Big Field with Boxer between the shafts, reached the junction of the two roads at the same time as the lorry. The latter crashed straight into the side of the cart, knocking both horse and vehicle over and catapulting Jim into the road. Miraculously no one was killed, but Boxer sustained a three-cornered cut high up on his hindquarters.

I came along just after he had been freed from the wreckage. A large lump of flesh, which must have weighed at least three to four pounds, hung down from a gaping hole. Unbelievably there did not appear to be another mark on him, not even a scratch. Asking me to hold Boxer, Jim walked round and literally folded the lump of flesh back from whence it had come. It fitted exactly, rather like putting a cork back in a bottle. There was very little blood. Quietly I led the terrified horse back to the farm, while Jim walked beside him with his hand on the wound. Luck was with us on two counts. First, we did not meet a motor vehicle of any class and, second, when we reached Britwell we found that Aubrey Ward, the vet, was there. He'd been called out to a cow with milk fever. He quickly examined the gelding and then deftly stitched the wound, doing such a wonderful job that six months later there was virtually no scar to be seen. Alas, however, there was one on Boxer's mind – he was terrified of lorries and so was no longer used on the roads.

We arrived at the field. Having entered and closed the gate behind us we spread out, about twenty yards apart. The horses stood tense and expectant, for they knew as well as us what was about to happen. At a given signal from Charlie Hawkins we slipped off the halters. Boxer reared, his massive hooves only inches above my head, before he wheeled and, bucking and kicking, thundered off with his companions. A wonderful sight! Those massive creatures, some six tons in all, were squealing with joy, jumping all four feet off the ground and capering like spring lambs. The ground shook as they raced away, to do two circuits of the field before finally slowing to a trot at the far end. Wheeling, nearly in line, they came up the centre, tails held high, heads tossing, nostrils dilated as they snorted in the sheer ecstasy of their freedom. Then, almost as though on command, down they went and rolled and rolled, their massive power-filled legs waving like demented shadowboxers. The ring of metal filled the air, as iron-clad hoof struck iron-clad hoof, and all the frustration of a winter's stalling was released. Sprey was the first to rise and, after a mighty shake, she started to graze. One by one the others followed, until all eight had their heads down enjoying God's bounty.

Charlie and the other two men departed, but I sat on the gate watching and deep in thought. War, I felt, was imminent.

Only one man of prominence appeared to realize where Baldwin's and Chamberlain's policies of disarmament and appeasement were leading us – Winston Churchill – and he was dubbed a warmonger! Vaguely I wondered if the eight gentle creatures, grazing so serenely, would be commandeered by the army.

I climbed down off the gate and wandered over to the contented munching group. None of them tried to walk away. I gave each one a pat and a lump of sugar – two for Sprey and Boxer, they were my favourites. I leaned against the former, my arms resting on her powerful withers as, after a careful examination of my pockets to make sure there was no more sugar, she returned to cropping the grass. Life seemed so good, with so much to come. I started my final exams at the university in a few weeks' time, but for what? To be blown to bits by some Nazi shell? Or would I go to South Africa at the end of September, as planned, in charge of a consignment of pedigree stock being shipped out there by Harry Hobson & Co.? Sprey took a step forward and literally jolted me back to the present.

Two larks were trilling overhead and a pigeon cooed from the shelter of a nearby fir. I glanced at my watch – it was twenty minutes to one. Lunch would be nearly over and I would not be popular with mother. But still I lingered, loth to leave. It was as though some unseen power held me, etching the tranquillity of the moment upon my mind for ever. A common enough sight, heavy horses grazing in a field, one viewed by thousands over many centuries – but for how much longer? At last I forced myself away. I felt depressed. It had been like a premonition of things to come that I did not want to accept, but knew I must. As I reached the road I did not look back. The picture would remain with me always.

MICHAEL F. TWIST, *THE SPACIOUS DAYS*, 1992

Champion Ploughman Jack House Reminisces

I was born in Dorset and my family moved to Fordingbridge when I was four-years-old. My earliest memories of working with horses go back to before I started school when I used to go out with my father and brother ploughing. When I got tired of walking behind they used to let me ride on the plough.

We moved back to between Wimborne and Blandford when I was eight and at the age of twelve to a farm at Downton. The boss farmed two farms of 1,300 acres in all. I started work in 1935 at the age of fourteen as one of the six carters. We had twenty-six horses to do all the farm work and I never did anything else until I was thirty-one. It was different than it is today – you had your own job.

We started work at 5.00 a.m. with feeding, mucking out and grooming. Breakfast was at 6.00 a.m. and back to work at 6.45 to harness up and out to work by 7.00 a.m. The boss used to look out of the bedroom window and give the working foreman the carter's orders first followed by more for the dairyman and daymen.

You'd see all the men setting off up the road to their different jobs, whether it be hedge-trimming or muck spreading or, in our case, ploughing, sowing or harrowing. We worked one shift right through to 3.30 with just a short break for lunch.

There was real comradeship in those days and terrific competition between the carters both for the way in which they kept their horses and for the best work done – especially with the ploughing. One of them would finish a turn early at lunch time and light a fire with twigs from the hedge for us all to sit round while we had our lunch. The horses had their nosebags but would wait till they got back to the stable at 4.00 p.m. for water.

Sometimes the boss would ask us to move the thrasher on the way home from a day's ploughing. We'd take trace harness and breeching with us in the morning. This was one of the hardest jobs on the farm for the horses. Two or three could move the thrasher on the roads, but during the war we had to build the ricks in the fields away from the buildings to lessen the risk of incendiary bombs causing a serious fire. The wet field conditions necessitated us using six horses to move the thrasher and one of my old horses, Captain, would start to shiver as soon as he saw it. He was a marvellous horse to pull but knew what the job entailed. As soon as he was in the shafts though, he was alright. The horses had to put everything into this job and stop immediately the thrasher reached the sticks which the feeder had pegged out, to position the machine for the next rick. Only one man used to lead the front horse in line.

If the weather was wet it was into the stable to oil harness or grease waggons. The boss kept his eye on the weather though and directly it was fine you were out to hitch on again.

It would be 4.00 p.m. by the time we got back to the stable after a day's work, and the horses were fed and groomed until about 5.00 p.m. They would lay in in the winter and we'd rack up for the night between 7.00 and 8.00 p.m. We were paid so much for the job – not hourly. Carters got 35/- a week while daymen got 28/-. For grass cutting in the summer, two of us would take four horses and work each pair alternately for two hours. While one pair was cutting the other carter would sharpen the knives and then change over with his horses.

In harvest time we'd take six horses out for the binder. While three were working at cutting the other three, who did the last shift on the previous day, would be tied up to the gate, and fed fresh clover heads. They'd then change over on the next shift. In the summer the horses would be led to water, we never carried a bucket for agricultural work.

The head and second shepherd and head and second dairyman would stay with their own jobs. The rest of the daymen would come out to help with the harvest, once their respective jobs were done. One hundred cows had to be milked twice a day by hand.

Farming must have paid though. Right up to 1940, when the boss got his first Fordson Tractor, all the work was done by horses. Their pace of work didn't damage the implements which lasted a lifetime. In 1943 he bought a combine drill. The carters never thought much of they. They said in a few years they'd grow nothing, for the new machines would squash all the life out of the land!

ANGELA GIFFORD, *HEAVY HORSE WORLD*, 1989

A Living Christmas Card: Brewery Shires Recall Victorian England

There's nothing so eye-catching on a city street as a smart pair of horses. When the horses are grey Shires standing over six feet at the shoulder, and the venue is Briggate, Leeds, effects are multiplied.

Joshua Tetley bought his first Shires when he bought his first brewery. That was in 1822, and beer has been brewed by Tetley's on the same site ever since. And the firm has kept faith with its Shires in unbroken line.

They were not universally called Shires in those far-off days. The first stud book, containing the pedigrees of stallions foaled previous to 1877, is called *The English Cart-Horse Stud Book*. Not until 1884 was the name Shire officially adopted by the breed society.

In the first thick stud book are listed seventy-two horses called Drayman. That is an indication of a prime function of the great horses; to haul the heavily-laden brewers' drays to quench the thirst of Victorian England.

At first the teams merely competed with other horses for right of way on city streets. Now they must withstand the noise and clamour of motors, remain calm when a bus bell rings a yard away, cope with surfaces made smooth for tyres.

Albert Hobson, thirty years with Tetley's Shires, claims that the complete horseman is a city driver. 'There are some very good farm horsemen, but they have a twenty-acre field to work in!' he says. Keen-eyed countrymen who drew ruler-straight brown furrows over a furlong of Yorkshire soil would not agree, but then Albert Hobson, product of the West Riding, delights in controversy.

He seeks the horses, buys them, feeds them and organizes their public outings. In 1983 Tetley's Shires attended over seventy-five functions. In autumn they returned to beer deliveries.

The firm owns ten Shires, all grey geldings. 'Everyone looks at a grey!' says Albert Hobson. He thinks they make more impression than a bay or a brown, and finds in general that motorists are cooperative where the big horses are concerned.

One December day in 1971, Leeds Corporation Planning and Traffic Management Committee had the temerity to seek a limit on the number of horse-drawn vehicles, threatening to introduce a law to that effect because there was none under which they could be banned.

Six pairs of Shires pull six Young's drays to celebrate the opening of a new restaurant at the Alexandra, Wimbledon. The brewery has now added Suffolks and Percherons to its stable. (Young & Co.'s Brewery plc)

Three mail bags full of letters on the topic arrived at the *Yorkshire Evening Post* office, the biggest number of protest letters in its history.

Not one agreed that the Tetley horses be banned or even curtailed. *Evening Post*, TV and Radio Leeds reporters climbed aboard the Tetley drays, to see what drivers of other vehicles had to say about the alleged hold-ups. Not one complained.

The Council withdrew, humbled. An influence that will not go away has been the Leeds motorway construction that demolished a number of small pubs and made the horses' routes more difficult. Yet they still ply their ancient trade, to the delight of all.

Tetley's prime pair are Mild and Bitter, both aged fourteen. They are veterans of several films and thousands of camera shots. Next come the six-year-olds Roger and Roller. Another six-year-old, Robert, was bought unbroken, yet within twelve months he had become leader in the six-horse team.

That is a responsible position. The lead pair is a long, long way ahead of the coachman strapped into his box seat. They must respond to voice as well as rein. For when Albert Hobson drives, he drives alone. He is not flanked by grooms, and the sight of his six-in-hand circling the green Great Yorkshire Show arena is matched only by that presented by that other team of greys, owned by Samuel Smith's of Tadcaster.

The Tetley Shires moved to their present stables twelve years ago. A range of nine loose boxes each twelve feet six inches square gives every comfort to the horses out of working hours. Above them is a huge loft, where is stored a year's supply of sweet hay, with broad bran and crushed oats to balance the ration.

Indispensable to the horses is Cyril Cooper, the farrier who succeeded Eric Plant. Having also served his time as wheelwright, Cyril Cooper maintains the vehicles against the hazards of Leeds streets.

Shoes last a month on average but, like humans, each horse varies. Some wear the heels, others the toes. All are a topic of conversation, and Tetley's harness room must be seen to be believed.

For the 15,000 annual visitors to the brewery, the Tetley stables are a highlight of their trip to Leeds.

EDWARD HART, *YORKSHIRE LIFE*, DECEMBER 1983

Harry Ranson Retires after a Lifetime with Young's Shire Horses

Harry Ranson, who has been head horsekeeper at the Brewery for more than twenty years, handed over the reins of Young's [Ram] winning show team to Peter Tribe at the beginning of the year.

Harry first got to know the stables at Young's at the age of three when he

Harry Ranson and friends on the day he retired as head horsekeeper to Young's in 1987. (Young & Co.'s Brewery plc)

was taken there by his father, Fred Ranson, who worked with the horses at the Brewery. Harry started work as a groom in 1940 after spending four years working on a stud farm in Lincolnshire. He and his boss had spent much time during the war years living in a loose box at the stables to ensure the safety of the horses at a time when fourten bombs were dropped on the Brewery.

In between fire-watching and serving with the Home Guard, Harry drove the horses on their regular deliveries to pubs, looked after their harness and worked in the blacksmith's shop.

After the war, Harry became the driver of Young's famous show team, which was unbeaten for four years between 1947 and 1951, working under Charlie Butler, whose achievements as head horsekeeper were recognized when Young's named a new pub after him in 1968.

Harry had taken over from Charlie Butler two years earlier, when Charlie retired, and in 1971 Harry received his own recognition with the award of the British Empire Medal for his role in setting up the Diamond Riding School for the Disabled at Carshalton in Surrey.

Harry's keen eye and sound judgement were responsible for the arrival of some remarkable horses at Young's, including the tallest in Britain, Goliath, and one of the stars of last year's Horse of the Year Show, Gilbert, who had been rescued from the knacker's yard only five years earlier. Harry travelled widely to find horses for his show team, as well as working horses, which still deliver beer in and around Wandsworth.

He is a life member of the Shire Horse Society and has judged at major horse shows throughout Britain. In his retirement Harry will never feel far from heavy horses; his judging is to continue, and among his commitments this year he will be adjudicating at the Royal International Horse Show at Birmingham.

Harry and his wife Doris have now moved from their home next to the Brewery stables in Wandsworth to spend their retirement in Ifold, West Sussex, where Harry is planning to enjoy a little private driving in the local lanes. He has two traps, a back to back gig and a brake and once the boxes are built he plans to acquire an appropriate horse, between 14 and 15 hands high and probably a Welsh cob.

At this early stage in his retirement Harry finds he is still waking early in the morning, with the horses' needs uppermost in his mind. 'At this time of year we are getting them fit for the Shire Horse Show at Peterborough,' he says. 'It is difficult to say what I shall miss the most,' Harry adds, 'but quite frankly I think it's the Brewery. It was a family brewery, a marvellous company with marvellous people, and we lived there for twenty years.'

ANON., HEAVY HORSE WORLD, 1987

Looking On . . . and Talking about Horses at Thorney

The smithy was traditionally a magnet for retired horsemen of the village. It retains its magic, as may be discovered at Thorney, Peterborough, when the travelling smith shoes Fred Harlock's Percherons – or any other heavies in that famous horse breeding district.

When I called, the yard was humming with heavy horse activity. Soham blacksmith Richard Gowing was shoeing a five-year-old brown Shire recently bought by well-known exhibitor Reg Coward. From Thorney village came saddler Dick Halford – his brother also makes harness at nearby Crowland – with a beautiful set of new blinders for a Percheron mare. Adding to the occasion were George Buckberry, Leslie Brown, Bob Doughty, Herbert Fisher, Bill Baxter and Bill Garner.

Among them they had probably a couple of centuries of horse experience, and had had several hundred heavies through their hands – Bob Doughty alone claimed over four hundred. He liked Clydesdales, but never handled Suffolks.

Bill Garner had travelled a Percheron stallion, walking one hundred and thirty to one hundred and fifty miles a week for the twelve-week season. He remembered the first Percheron imports following the first world war, and how they did not really catch on until the first crop of foals was produced.

The Shires of those days were much heavier legged. After work they would be walked through a pond three at a time, the horseman riding the nearside horse, to wash the mud off their fetlocks. In winter the clagging soil would freeze and rattle. On one farm, twenty-two working horses were kept in four stables, and all were turned out with tails plaited with a bit of straw.

The farmers of those days expected the teams to leave their stable by 7 am, and were equally insistent that they returned by 2.30 pm. Obtaining extra rations for his horses was part of the keen horseman's stock-in-trade; he would carry an extra sack of corn a considerable distance, and many a bag of pig meal was diverted to the stables. Bob Baxter admitted to taking a plasticine impression of the barn key, and having the local locksmith copy it on the pretext of Crowland Abbey connections!

Among all the fun, and a few rather tall stories, an invaluable fund of practical horsemanship emerges.

'Get plenty of flesh on your horses by Christmas. If you do, they can winter well, but, if not, they cannot improve before spring.' . . . 'Yoke young horses very carefully at first. Jibbers are made by putting them straight into something that they can't move, like a cart with a heavy load of muck.' . . . 'Put on the collars before breakfast, to warm up before yoking.'

Driving a team with only one rein seems a peculiarly East Anglian art. Though a young horse might be broken with a rein either side in the conventional way, it soon took its place in the team with only one line used for three or even four horses abreast. In a four-horse team, a line was used only on the third horse, the others having false lines from their bearing reins to the heel tree or swingletree of the horse being driven.

When three were driven in line, there was a rein only to the lead or farest horse, hitched to the curb chain running behind the jaw. The centre horse in line was the pin horse, the shaft horse being last. To turn the team to the left, a steady pull on the line and the words 'Come here' were used. To turn right, the command was 'Eet up' combined with gentle chucks or shakes of the line.

Specially reliable horses were used for particular jobs, the most memorable of which followed a severe thunderstorm at Shapland Wash, when fourteen young horses at pasture took fright and finished up in the deep dykes which were the only boundaries. To extricate them, two horses and a cart were used, with a rope over the cart front to give the necessary height to haul the animals to dry land. All were rescued safely. On another occasion a pony was struck by lightning while drinking, and took no water for the next three weeks.

Understandably, the knot of old stagers were somewhat contemptuous of modern farming practice.

'We drilled sixteen acres a day using four horses in a six foot six inch-drill – two in front and two behind and a lad walking between the lead pair. There was no stopping at the ends except to fill with seed, and no working till 8 pm. Our stint was 7.30 to 2.30, and we daren't make a bad job because the other chaps would come round on Sunday morning to look at it' recalled Bob Doughty.

If the teams were due to deliver corn the next day, the horsemen would sit up half the night cleaning their brasses. Loads of two-and-a-half to three tons were common, but much heavier weights were involved moving threshing tackle. The portable engines had to be dragged by a fourteen-horse team.

Threshing corn called for fine weather, the wet-day job being a visit to the blacksmith's. As every other farmer in the neighbourhood had the same idea, long queues accumulated, with much advice on how to manage other's horses. Today these East Anglian men of the land turn their fund of knowledge to Fred Harlock's Percheron stud, and rejoice with him over the four live foals born this year from four mares, and at the show ring successes of Abbeythorne Princess and her young offspring, Countess.

EDWARD HART, *HEAVY HORSE & DRIVING*, 1977

The One Thing I Would Miss . . .

The one thing that I would miss most in this modern world would be the most simple and happiest of any occupations, walking behind the plough pulled by two good horses and singing at the top of my voice one of the old country songs.

And the horses would gently plod on getting slower and slower as the singer continues with each verse and chorus, the song would end, the horses pick up speed, the echoes would die away but the contentment would remain and you would be just another farm lad.

HARRY REFFOLD, *PIE FOR BREAKFAST*, 1984

'Feel their Oats'

No one man, however strong and skilful, can stop two horses weighing the best part of a ton apiece if they really mean to go. And Shires, though models of calm and good behaviour most of the time, can on occasion 'feel their oats' just as much as any other horse. Charlie Ruocco for instance has a vivid memory of driving a pair of horses across Tower Bridge when, because of some Royal

Steadiness and reliability in every muscle.

birthday, the guns in the Tower began to fire a salute. 'I never found out whose birthday it was,' says Charlie – 'or how old he may have been. Because by the time they fired the third shot we were off, full tilt, across the bridge. There were traffic lights at the far end and they only turned green in the nick of time. I couldn't have gone a yard slower and it took me half a mile to pull up!'

JOHN OAKSEY, PRIDE OF THE SHIRES, 1980

Captain Peter Courage

Some men, and horses, appear indestructible, bulwarks against time and its machinations. Such was Captain Peter Courage, which made news of his death aged sixty-five all the more of a shock.

Captain Courage was well named. He led a full life among horses, and was a thrusting rider and highly competent judge of those heavyweight hunters needed to carry his considerable frame.

During the Second World War he served in North Africa and the Middle East, taking part in many hair-raising expeditions, losing an eye in the process. Thereafter (and possibly before) he didn't give a damn for any man.

He started hunting aged sixteen, and became Master of Foxhounds in North Yorkshire, President of his local Kirkby Fleetham show and of the Shire Horse

Spring and Autumn from a tile panel painted by Albert Siater for Longton Swimming Baths, Stoke-on-Trent, 1886.

17

Society in a difficult period, 1965–6. He later became chairman of the Stud Book Editing Committee, a post he held to the end.

The Shire Stallion Premium Scheme, Blood Grouping Scheme and Stallion Approval Scheme were all brought in during his reign. At a more personal level, Captain Courage was largely responsible for new stables at Courages' Alton brewery, and the change from Clydesdales to Shires.

Equally at home with fellow brewery directors, horse-keeping farmers, or their grooms, Captain Peter spared no effort in any equine business. At one horse function, officials were asked to wear identifying lapel badges. Captain Peter demurred. 'Every silly beggar knows me!' he said. And we did. Now we miss him, his stalwart figure and forthright greeting, more than we can ever say.

EDWARD HART, *HEAVY HORSE WORLD*, 1987

Ploughing and Pressing

At the age of fifteen, I was in farm service at Finningley Park Farm. I was hired for one year, and at the end of each year, we would go to the Doncaster Hirings. Sometimes you were lucky enough to get a good place to work together with good food, other times not so lucky. Work was hard, with very little pay. I had eight shillings per week plus my food when I worked at Finningley.

The following year, I was hired by a foreman who worked for H. Barker & Sons – farmers of Edderthorpe, nr. Darfield, Barnsley. My pay was ten shillings per week. I lodged with the local gamekeeper. Up to now this was my best year.

Whilst I was at Edderthorpe, I learned more about ploughing. I was with one of the best tutors anyone could have. He was called Arthur Sykes. He taught me a lot. We had about one hundred and eighty acres of seed land, which had been sheep grazing for two years. As one lot was ploughed up, another was ready for the sheep in the Spring – this happened every year. Once we had the land we planted winter wheat or winter oats. There were four of us on the job – Arthur, myself, Bill Wincupp and another boy.

Arthur had a single furrow Cook A plough – long breast for seaming. Bill Wincupp had a 2 furrow – same model – yours truly had the same as Arthur, and the 'old boy' had a 4 wheel press which had a drill box on. He used to follow us, taking four furrows, same as the press. We had one horse in the shafts and one yoked to the other side of the press. It was known as 'ploughing and pressing'. We were ploughing, pressing and drilling, all in one operation. Arthur used to set all the rigs, and I used to finish all the furrows. Arthur got me finishing furrows to a fine art. He then showed me how to set a rig. The plough had two wheels on. He could set the plough up so that he didn't have to hold the hales – just drive his horse straight for the 'Wad Sticks'. He got me doing the same, and when I'd finished he told me I was nearly as good as he was.

JOHN J. CREASER, *SIXTY YEARS IN THE ISLE*, 1990

Another Runaway

It was the same harvest that I had another runaway: it was in Old Sledmere field. We had sown it with barley, so it had to be reaped, a light crop, half of it eaten off by rabbits. We pulled in with our binders. The field had quite a large dale across one side, too steep to grow anything on, and another side dropped steeply to the roadside. But the part that we were cutting was fairly level, so off we went, four horses all fit and fresh. Two of them could nearly have managed, but four it was: a nice day.

I was content and thinking about nothing in particular when I clapped the ends of the reins together. The four of them shot off like a gun across the field, through the standing corn. My reaper man Jim pushed the lever to put it out of gear and then dropped the reaper points as near to the ground as possible so that if I was thrown off I would not be dragged underneath the machine.

But Tidy, the mare I was riding, was quite a nimble type and she kept her feet and we hit no rabbit holes. Across the field we stormed, across to the roadside fall. That was when we all started to worry, because we all knew that if they started to go down the bank the whole lot would finish at the bottom in one ghastly heap, horses, reaper and myself.

We were almost to the edge, when there was a slackening of speed. Jim had done his job properly. The points protecting the knives, by just skimming the soil, had gathered so much of the standing corn that it had been acting as a top working brake, and four horses could only gallop and pull a dead weight of half a ton or more for a certain distance before either weariness or sense caught up with them. They came to a stop, with the leading pair of horses having their forefeet on the edge, blowing and steaming, but all of them and myself were in one piece, unharmed.

HARRY REFFOLD, 1984

The Great War and After

The world conflict of 1914–18 ended the era of unlimited skilled labour. Grooms and their horses died together in Flanders, where massive animals were less well adapted to the horrific conditions than cleaner-legged ones.

19

A flood of 'demobbed' horses poured on to the market at the war's end, as uncontrolled as the mass of soldiers seeking in vain for 'the land fit for heroes', or even a job of any sort. The number of entries in the *Shire Horse Society Stud Book* reached its all-time peak in 1920 and 1921, but not until the late 1920s did the position sort itself out, and demand and supply of draught horses reach some sort of equilibrium.

In the poverty-stricken countryside that existed until the mid-1930s, the best Shire studs kept their heads above water, but usually from outside finance rather than horse breeding. The big shows still attracted large classes, but there was no spare cash for experiment, and survival rather than improvement was the order of the day.

EDWARD HART, *THE BOOK OF THE HEAVY HORSE*, 1986

The Story of Corn

Our awareness of the long ancestry of the ploughman is somehow more alert when we see a pair of horses pulling at the end of his reins.

Such an awareness was very present with me yesterday when, in the course of a single mile, I came upon as many as five ploughmen driving their ploughs, two horses abreast, across the wheaten stubble. In these days, when there are wide acres everywhere given over to tractor cultivation, with hardly a man in the whole length and breadth of them capable of handling a plough, this fact in itself would be worth recording. In East Anglia at least, I thought, though all the rest of England turn pasture or cultivate with the tractor, horse-ploughing is not yet altogether a thing of the past. And where there are horse-ploughmen there is still earth-wisdom, for no man is more closely or more patiently occupied with the ground beneath his feet and the wheeling weather over his head.

'It's a heavy, wet old field,' one of the ploughmen said to me, when he had called Boxer and Gipsy to a halt at the headland and with one hand was leisurely applying the scraper to the clogged coulter: 'it's a heavy, wet old field, and it wants drainin' badly. But then, so do a lot more round here. Come winter, the water will stand in these furrows like a pond. Drainin' and manurin', they're both nigh done away with these days; but you won't never get good crops without 'em, leastways not to my way of thinkin'. Why, there's some fields over on the next farm ain't smelt a load of manure these forty years! Old Tom Philby was talking about it last night, up at the 'Wheatsheaf': nothin' but a bit of artificial. 'Tain't good enough: 'tain't fair on the land.'

Lightly he shook the reins. Boxer seemed to take a long time to understand: then the muscles rippled down his sturdy flanks, he strained forward, with

Gipsy gently coming up beside him, and the dark earth flowed back from the cleaving share, so smoothly and so evenly that the only possible likeness was to some lazy uncurling wave of the sea. For awhile I stood watching the ploughman retreat into the distance, where the field bordered on to a wood, mistily blue in the October sunshine, while a second ploughman advanced out of the shadow some four or five furrows away. Before such an ageless scene it was impossible not to be glad that no tractor broke the pregnant quiet. The only sound was of the men speaking to their horses at the headlands, and then, if your ear could catch it, the subdued harmony of hoof and blade and turning clod.

C. HENRY WARREN, *CORN COUNTRY*, 1940

Horses are Strange Creatures

During the 1920s every farm had its full quota of working horses and the harness maker was kept busy making new harness and doing repairs. But it wasn't long before the recently introduced tractors took over much of the work. Many horses became redundant and some were slaughtered. During the war however horses made a bit of a comeback while fuel oil was rationed. It was at this time that I was able to buy some nice Welsh colts, and having

Clydesdales at work.

21

broken them and used them for a time, I sold them again for a nice profit. I was fortunate to have an old experienced horseman called 'Duke' Capon working for me who helped with this schooling, and between us we were able to break and sell several horses during the war years. We also bred a few foals, which in due course found a ready sale.

Horse breaking is a skilled and sometimes dangerous job, but even the tricky bits have their lighter side – like the day Duke and I were lunging a splendid three-year-old Percheron colt on a ploughed field. 'Lunging' consists of connecting a long rein to each side of the horse's 'bit'; then with one man each side, the horse is made to trot in a wide circle, one man standing still in the centre and the other running smartly round on the outside. By alternating the direction of the drive (clockwise or anti-clockwise), the horse is trained to respond to the rein on either side, and the men are rested by taking alternate positions.

The reason for using a ploughed field was to make heavy going for the colt and slow him down to a speed at which we could keep up with him. During Duke's turn on the outer circle something suddenly frightened the colt and he shot forward, pulled Duke flat on his stomach and dragged him along. He was wearing a pair of old fashioned corduroy trousers with a wide button-up flap instead of 'flies' – and as he was dragged along, the flap became partially unfastened and the front of his trousers filled up with loose soil. By the time I had stopped the colt he had accumulated such a weight of soil that he couldn't get up – and we had to empty his flap before we could resume operations.

. . . When we were children, my sisters and I used to go round every year selling 'violet' plums. Having shaken them from the trees, with father's help, we would harness old Tom horse into the cart and 'hawk' the plums around the village.

Old Tom Horse pulled a London tram till he was twenty years old, and when he retired from the streets Uncle George bought him for £5 and he lived and worked on our holding for a further fifteen years. He finally became afflicted with the 'farcy', a painful swelling of the leg akin to gout in humans. He lay down on the meadow one Saturday evening and couldn't get up again. Father sent for a Knacker, but he would not come out till the Monday morning. The old horse was in such misery that Father would not wait for the knacker with his 'humane killer' and asked the local butcher – Ted Dann – to end the poor old chap's suffering with his pole-axe, the tool that was used in those days to slaughter cattle. It was illegal, of course, to use such a thing on a horse, but it was all over in a second – so what did it matter?

Old Tom would not allow us boys to catch him on the meadow, but would rush at us with his teeth bared and eyes ablaze, thus effectively avoiding capture. But my father could always halter him without any trouble. I think the old horse had it in for us boys because when we did get him into the cart we would give him a sharp smack with a stick on his backside. Invariably his tail shot up simultaneously with a loud emission of wind which could be heard for a considerable distance – and caused much merriment to his tormentors.

Horses are strange creatures, reacting in predictable ways to various stimuli. Ernest Smith, a butcher, had a smart roan pony called Strawberry. Ernest's son Harold and I were riding down towards Hethersett station in a trap pulled by Strawberry one day and I stood up to get a better view of a train approaching the station. As I stood balanced in the trap Harold gave a low whistle. The pony stopped dead in her tracks and started to 'stale', pitching me over the front of the cart and landing me between her back legs. Luckily I wasn't hurt, but my enthusiasm for train spotting was a bit dampened!

It was a quite usual practice among old horsemen to whistle softly to make their horses relieve themselves before going into the stable. Years later I was in hospital recovering from an operation, and in the next bed was an old horseman who had undergone an operation two days before. Since his operation he had been unable to pass water and the nurses were using all sorts of ruses, like turning on the water taps, to start him off – but without success. Suddenly I had an inspiration – I gave the same low whistle I had often used for my horses – and the old chap started to urinate almost immediately. 'Blast, you've done it,' he cried, and filled his bottle to the brim.

Bob Denmark had retired before I left school. He had been a farm worker all his life, mostly with horses, and once told me that he never saw his home in daylight for the six winter months of the year. He used to get up at 4 o'clock in the morning, walk to work in time to feed his horses at 5 o'clock and be ready to turn out for work at 6.30. After a day's work finishing at 6 p.m., and sometimes using two teams of horses alternately, he would 'bait' his horses again, then groom them, often not reaching home until 7.30 in the evening. Despite the long hours, he would often re-visit the farm during the night if a sick horse needed attention or a mare was expected to foal. For this he was paid 12/- a week and 1/- a week extra if he cut his own chaff.

ROBERT C. RICHARDSON, *SOME FELL ON STONY GROUND*, 1978

The Last of the Line

Whenever a breed or species is driven to the brink of extinction there must inevitably come a time when the doubtful distinction of being the last of the line rests upon a single survivor. In the case of the railway horse it was a brown and white gelding named 'Charlie', the last shunting horse of three previously employed at Newmarket goods station in Suffolk. On 21 February 1967, Charlie shunted his own horsebox onto the train taking him from Newmarket station to retirement pastures.

Almost two years previously a similar scene had taken place when Charlie had drawn his stable companion's horsebox, and 'Butch', an eighteen-year-old bay, had left for Somerset, destination, Clare Hall, Ston Easton, the home of Mr John Hippisley, a railway officer on BR Eastern Region.

If things had worked out as planned, the last three of Newmarket's shunt horses would have gone into honourable retirement, but 'Tommy' had dropped dead soon after taking part in the 1961 Horse of the Year Show, at Wembley. With Tommy's demise (from natural causes, not overwork) Butch and Charlie shared the diminishing work-load, shunting horseboxes taking runners to meetings such as Leicester, Doncaster or Haydock Park (although many now went by road or air) and dealing with a few daily wagonloads of mixed goods.

Little is known about the origins of Tommy and Butch, but by a quirk of fate the career of Charlie has been traced from start to finish. While in retirement at Clare Hall, whence he had followed Butch (who died before Charlie arrived there), he was visited by an 87-year-old man who had bought him as a three-year-old at Keynsham Market, and worked him on a farm at Bridgwater. At about six years of age Charlie had been sold into railway service and commenced his duties as a shunt horse at Camden Town goods yard in London. After some time in the south he was transferred to Birmingham, thence to Bolton, to Bristol in the West Country, then northwards again to Liverpool. His last years were spent in East Anglia, firstly at Diss, and finally Newmarket. Charlie was born in Somerset, at Castle Carey, and so after working eighteen years on the railway, had returned to his native county.

A cross-breed, basically a Clydesdale, showing little feather around the hoof, he was not a big horse, weighing only 16 cwt and standing 17 hands high. But his was an ideal conformation for a shunt horse, and he possessed an equable temper and an obedient nature, being well regarded by his many handlers. At Newmarket his driver was Lawrence (Lol) Kelly, an experienced horseman who had once been an apprentice in a racing stable. Charlie couldn't have been in better or more kindly hands.

In his last years, Charlie was very much a celebrity, not only with children, who would queue after school for rides, but also well known through television to nationwide audiences. A few weeks before he retired, Charlie was visited by the BBC 'Tonight' television team, and Lol Kelly was interviewed by Fyfe Robertson, the celebrated broadcaster. But the euphoria did not last; and Charlie soon faded from the headlines.

Lol Kelly remembers that both horses were docile, but with marked idiosyncrasies. For instance, Charlie would have a go at anything, but Butch had his off days, for he suffered with his back. He had been mis-handled at some time or another, and Lol explained the skills of an experienced shunt horse driver. The operation began by hooking the tug chain from the hames onto the box car. Then the driver would take a firm hold of the reins, pulling well back, and letting the horse move gently forward until it was down almost on its knees with hindlegs extended. Sometimes, the driver didn't keep a firm hold and then the horse would snatch forward, the load remaining static. 'It would then be like the horse hitting a brick wall,' said Lol.

He went to see Charlie in Somerset where, in retirement at Clare Hall, he shared a paddock with two donkeys, several riding ponies, and a cow. Lol leant over the gate and called out to him. 'Immediately Charlie stuck up his head, looked around and pricked up his ears. I called him again, and he came galloping over to me.'

While at Clare Hall, Charlie was honoured with the CDM (Cadbury's Dairy Milk) Award, a promotional gimmick used in an advertising campaign of the time. Charlie was also much sought after to appear at shows and fetes, where he was paraded around the ring, raising money for various charities.

Lol Kelly's proudest moment was when he appeared with Charlie in the parade of horse personalities at the Wembley Horse of the Year Show, in 1965, before HRH Princess Margaret.

The massive Shire horses made him look like a pony. But every night amongst big name champions, Charlie was everybody's darling. He had many admirers during the day, too, bringing him lumps of sugar and tit-bits.

But Mr Kelly's most poignant memory is the parting gift left for Charlie at the station gate by Mr H.E. Pringle, the Newmarket corn merchant. There was a sack of oats, a bunch of carrots, a bale of hay, and horse cubes to sustain Charlie during his long journey to Somerset.

Said Lol:

I'll always be proud of Charlie. I'm conscious of the years of hard work put in by many thousands of other railway horses and their drivers. They did their job of work unnoticed.

But Charlie, God bless him, he'll never be forgotten. He was truly the last of the line.

BRYAN HOLDEN, *THE LONG HAUL*, 1985

Harry Rockliff in the Vale of York

A lover of the working horse, he kept his Shire teams together, but gone was the remunerative market for the five-year-old, quiet in all gears and suited to city work. All breeders suffered, from the big pedigree stud owners to the working farmers.

'A change from drawing the Lord Mayor's coach!' say the Whitbread Shires. (Nicholas Redman, Archivist, Whitbread plc)

One of Harry Rockliff's stories touches the heartstrings. Half a dozen unbroken two- and three-year-old Shires were out watering in the confined farm yard. They would rear, kick and stamp and prance in their high spirits, then gallop in concert through the open gate. One day a small girl, a toddler, escaped from her mother's vigilance and crawled across the gateway. The young horses set off in their usual style, flat out for the gate with a pounding of great hooves, when from their midst an old Shire mare thrust herself to the fore. She jumped right over the little girl and parted the tearaways on either side.

Suffice it to say that that mare was never sold. She had thirteen foals in fourteen years, and an intelligence comparable to Mr Frome's mare, described in the early *Clydesdale Stud Book* as being 'as wise as a man'.

On the small farm with insufficient, lame or worn-out horses, cutting corn was hell. We should always remember that horses in general have a far better time today than when they were the sole means of power. Then, they sometimes had to work when over-stressed or unsound. It was not deliberate cruelty, simply that the work had to be done and the harvest won somehow.

The scope for inequality and abuse in the old landlord/tenant system is ready fuel for its critics. They should remember the other side of the coin. Harry Rockliff told of how the owner of Beningbrough Hall kept spare teams of Shires on his home farm, so that a tenant could always be told 'Go to the home farm for a horse' if one of his own became lame at a busy time.

EDWARD HART, 1986

The Shire Stallion

The magnificent shire stallion is a very early memory. As far back as I can remember I seem to have been thrilled by these grand creatures. Whenever one went striding past the farm gate, bedecked with ribbons and plaits, I would follow it as far as possible, and try to beg a card from its attendant groom. This card usually bore a photograph of the stallion and its pedigree and points. As boys we used to discuss stallions and their qualities as boys today discuss aeroplanes.

Twice a year a parade of stallions was held in Silk-town. From all over east and mid-Cheshire they were brought to this parade, there to show off their paces and points to the crowds of farmers and horsey folk gathered for the occasion. The parade was held in a side street, which as a rule was quiet; but running parallel with it was a railway, whose tracks, unfortunately, were visible from the street. The stallions were drawn up in a line, with their heads facing the pavement, at intervals of twelve to fifteen yards. A crowd of farmers would gather round each horse and there was much feeling of the stallions' leg bones, examination of hooves, and discussions with the grooms on the horses' particular qualities. Cards of pedigree were handed round, but never to boys who coveted them.

But when the London express went shrieking past, the stallions would rear and plunge and scatter the farmers in all directions. A rearing stallion is an impressive sight, and many times have I watched them, half expecting to see the groom smashed by the huge hooves as they descended. At intervals each stallion would be trotted briskly up and down the street, and his action would come in for much criticism from the watching farmers.

The years went by and mechanical power was ousting the horse from the street and, to a lesser degree, from the farm. Foals were not so much in demand, and farmers were not so interested in stallions. The attendance of both horses and farmers at the parade gradually dwindled, until finally it was decided that it was not worth while to bring the horses into the town. And so, much to my regret, the parades were discontinued.

However, the sight of a shire stallion striding through the country lanes is not yet an unfamiliar one, and whenever I see one I always want to draw him.

His beautiful proportions, strong muscles, glossy coat and fine rhythmic action never fail to excite me, and I have drawn him, painted him, etched him and engraved him on wood.

To see him in all his glory you should go to a big agricultural show. There he will be all be-ribboned, plaited, cockaded, polished and combed, a thing of amazing strength and beauty.

C.F. TUNNICLIFFE, *MY COUNTRY BOOK*, 1942

A First Purchase

Broken to ride and drive! How on earth could that be? She was only a two-year-old. I stood gaping at this gorgeous animal, clutching the catalogue and listening to the seller talking of her virtues to a prospective buyer. 'Been ridden by my ten-year-old son: no problems! Driven around the streets of Carlisle by the same boy: no problems!'

Was I hearing correctly? I wonder how many folk would trust a ten-year-old boy to a two-year-old filly in Carlisle, or a two-year-old filly to a ten-year-old boy, for that matter?

I was standing by a pen during Wigton market's October sale. Inside was a piebald. She was 14.3 hands, strongly built, heavy boned and was a striking colour, about 80 per cent white and 20 per cent black.

Certainly she seemed kind, as people walked in and out of her stall, prodding and poking, lifting feet, looking at teeth, eyes and ears, picking up her tail and feeling her legs. She was by a black Clydesdale stallion out of a skewbald pony mare, and she was lovely.

And I was looking for a horse. I'd always liked coloured horses. I also love heavy horses, but would certainly not dream of buying a purebred. I wanted a female, and preferably a young horse to train on. It all seemed too good to be true.

Now, one thing was certainly true, and that was that I didn't (and still don't) know enough to buy an unknown horse at a public auction, and I needed help. There were about 180 lots to go before her turn. I had a little time and so I scoured the sale. Fortunately a number of my horsey friends were there. One after another they were asked if they would go and look at the filly. One after another they came back with their reports, which all added up to approval. I wanted her, and if I had the money, I was to go ahead. The more experienced gave me a price limit. It was higher than I expected, but if I did this, that and the other, financially I could manage.

Nerve. I needed nerve. My knees were a bit wobbly as she was led from her pen and joined the queue for the sale ring. The ringside was so packed that I

The Half-Clydesdale piebald mare Queenie, driven by Audrey Hart.

wondered if I'd ever be through the crowd in time for her turn. I was. My throat was parched and dry. She was next. The gate opened and the ten-year-old boy rode her in, no saddle or bridle, only a headcollar. She walked proudly round and round. I was fascinated. So fascinated, I had almost forgotten about the bidding. It had raced away and I began to wonder what was happening.

The bidding stopped suddenly, at £100 more than my 'ceiling'. The reports from my advisers rang in my ears. The sight of her proud walk filled my eyes. I bid. My first bid, and I knew it would be my last. There was a silence. The auctioneer broke it, cajoling others to bid. But they didn't, and she was mine.

Later, after a mad dash to arrange transport, and following a visit to a building society in town and complicated discussions at a bank, she was paid for. I found her tied up in a pen in a corner of the market, and stood by her, listening with some pride to comments of passers-by. One man even tried to buy her from me. He had apparently missed the sale and brandished fistfuls of ten pound notes. But she was mine and not for sale.

Luckily, I caught sight of the vendors just as they were leaving the market. I deluged them with questions. They were as helpful as they could be. 'What's her name?' No one had mentioned it. I was told she had been named by 'grandfather' after the best horse he had ever had, and he had thought she might come as good as that one, one day. I hope so, my Queenie.

AUDREY HART, *CARRIAGE DRIVING*, 1988

two

When It All Began

Even in the eighteenth century, definite forms of cart-horses were recognized. It was too early to call them breeds; that came later, and was formalized by the breed societies.

Some good writing occurred in those years, invariably by men; women did not grace the writing scene until later, at least not as far as horses were concerned. These authors were authoritative on several classes of stock, which avoided that boring phenomenon, the one-breed fanatic, found among cattle and sheep breeders as well as among horse people.

Though few men travelled far, those who did took their time, and understood what they saw. George Culley was one, and in 1794 his *Observations on Live Stock* was published. He listed both Clydesdale and Suffolk Punch, but not Shire as such. Progenitors of that breed were referred to as 'The Heavy BLACK HORSES, almost universally bred throughout the midland counties'.

Arthur Young, in his *Tours*, 1770, itemized the stocking of a Vale of Evesham farm which included 26 horses at £15 each, 4 wagons (one a broad-wheeled one) for £100, and 2 broad-wheel carts totalling £24.

Since then the men who seldom ventured further than their nearest market town, except when they changed jobs, have recorded their experiences. Often disclaiming literary skill, their writings ring true, and convey the effort, hardships, laughter and leg-pulling involved in the world of the working horse.

Though some of these characters adapted happily to the role of tractor driver, they have only to see a pair at a ploughing match, or a heavy breed foal on a May pasture, or a well-horsed dray on the road, to be transported back to those days when their whole lives revolved around their big horses.

The Dray-horse

The London Dray-horse (and all the horses of the same size and character used in Liverpool and Manchester) is recruited from the largest specimens of the true Shire horse, slow, stately, ponderous, not less than 17 hands high, often 18 hands; he is in horses what a corporal major of Life Guards is to a private of Dragoons.

Weight in the brewers' horses is essential, because they have to move great weights for short distances, and the shaft-horse frequently has to hold up and back and turn with enormous loads; for although barrels do not look very large, when filled with beer their gravity is far in excess of the idea conveyed by their bulk. No doubt something is due to fashion and tradition, in the employment of these equine giants by the beer kings of London. First-class farmers, who plough the stiffest land deeply, who are not content with what Mr Mechi called 'the traditional three inches of agricultural pie-crust', consider that 16 hands high is high enough for the very best plough or cart team, although they do not object to an additional inch in an active, well-shaped animal.

Formerly the twelve great brewing firms, familiarly known as the 'Beer Kings of London', used to be as particular about the colours and matchings of their dray-horses as of their own four-in-hands or the Court chariot pairs of their titled wives: one was celebrated for a black, the original dray-horse colour; another for a brown, a roan, a grey, or chestnut team. But at present such is the demand for horses of this class, that they are compelled to be content with any colour, and to moderate the old standard of height. The parade of teams belonging to Liverpool merchants, on the occasion of the annual show of the Royal Agricultural Society of England being held in the year 1877, was probably the finest gathering of dray-horses ever witnessed.

Following the plan adopted in preparing this work, of going to headquarters for special information, a set of queries were forwarded to Mr James Moore, junr., the veterinary superintendent of Messrs Barclay, Perkins, & Co.'s stud of brewery dray-horses, to which he has, with the sanction of the firm, kindly returned the following pithy answers:-

'Heavy draught-horses suitable for dray work are English bred, and are generally from Wiltshire, Berkshire, Oxfordshire, Herefordshire, Lincolnshire, and Yorkshire; bred by farmers who in many instances are horse-dealers.

'They are bought at five to six years of age, and last about ten years.

'One horse here stood 18 hands high, and weighed nearly 18 cwt. He was a fine handsome red (or strawberry) roan horse, named 'Baly'. When Garibaldi visited the brewery, in 1864, he particularly noticed the horse, and he was ever afterwards known as Garibaldi. He was about seventeen years old when he died, in 1870.

'There are several horses at the present time in the brewery that stand 17½ hands high, and they are mostly of a roan colour.

'No mares are used in the brewery.

'Horses that are used for our country work travel from twenty-five to thirty miles on some days. It is rather difficult to say what distance the horses used for town work travel.

'The weight drawn in a two-wheeled dray is from 3 tons 16 cwt. to 4 tons; two horses used, sometimes three.

'The weight drawn in a four-wheel van is from 6 tons to 6 tons 10 cwt.; three horses are used, sometimes four.

'Their food consists of –

Oats, 13 lbs, beans, 6lbs, maize, 3 lbs =   22 lbs per day per horse.
Clover chaff, about   15   "   "   "
                                                  37   "   "   "

Sometimes peas are given, then either beans or maize are stopped.

'From April to September about two thousand bundles of green tares are consumed amongst the sick and rest horses.

'From May to August three hundred bundles of green tares are given to all the horses every week for about fourteen or fifteen weeks; one bundle is given to each horse on Saturday evening, and one on Sunday morning. Carrots are occasionally given.

'The cost of feeding, including the above items, amounts to about three shillings per horse per day.

'Brewers' horses are not, as you suggest, kept for ornament, but for work.

'Shoeing costs about one shilling and eightpence per week, being about fifty-nine shoes per horse per year. As a matter of course, some horses wear their shoes out sooner than others.

'The diseases to which brewers' dray-horses are subject are catarrh, influenza, bronchitis, congestion of the lungs (more in summer from violent exertion), nephritis, hepatitis, weed, cellulitis, colic (more cases of colic on commencing green food), sandcracks, treads, quittors, and wounds from picking up nails, stones, and other foreign agents in the streets. We have had several cases of ruptured livers between 1867 and 1874, the livers in these cases weighing respectively 73 lbs, 89 lbs, 82 lbs, 61 lbs, and 101 lbs.

'Horses will drink beer if they can get it. We generally give it when they are recovering from an illness, and with beneficial results.

'The vulgar idea which exists that brewers' horses are fed upon wet grains is incorrect.

'Dray-horses are not so heavy as they used to be; they are shorter and stouter. The animal known as a 'little big horse' is preferred; a smaller horse is more active, and gets over the ground quicker; this accounts for the great demand at the present time for the Clydesdale breed.

'I think the popular opinion that roans, red and blue, are more hardy than horses of other colours, is correct.

'We use neither bearing-reins, nor winkers on the bridles'.

SAMUEL SIDNEY, *THE BOOK OF THE HORSE*, 1880S

Mr Bakewell

Bakewell's achievements in livestock improvement extended to horses and pigs. As oxen began to be replaced by horses there was increasing demand for improved types, whether for the farm, the town or the army. Up till Bakewell's time the horse-breeder had been mainly concerned with types suitable for hunting, racing, coaching, and the army. Culley records how Bakewell was impressed by some Dutch black coach stallions which had been brought to Leicestershire from Holland by one of the Earls of Huntingdon, for use by his tenants. These had sired horses of a very good type and Bakewell, having seen them, characteristically went off to Holland and bought several mares of the same breed. These he used, by crossing, to improve the black heavy horses native to his own county. Once again, by continued selection and careful breeding, he evolved a distinctive type of draught horse which met a demand from the army as well as for the farm. He got rid of much of length and looseness of form, and also long, thick, hairy legs, ultimately breeding a more compact, shorter-limbed and more active animal and for which he claimed better constitution. He was criticized by those who equated bulk or weight with strength. Marshall has left on record his appreciation in the following statement:

King, the tallest living horse at 19.2 hands high (*Guinness Book of Records*, 1994).

33

The handsomest horse I have seen of this breed (the Leicestershire black cart-horse) and perhaps the most picturable horse of this kind bred in this island, was a stallion of Mr Bakewell named K. He was in reality, the fancied War horse of the German painters; who in the luxuriance of imagination, never perhaps excelled the natural grandeur of this horse. A man of moderate size seemed to shrink behind his fore end, which rose so perfectly upright that his ears stood (as Mr Bakewell says every horse's ought to stand) perpendicularly over his fore feet. It may be said, with little latitude, that in grandeur and symmetry of form, viewed as a picturable object he exceeded as far as the horse which this superior breeder had the honour of showing to his Majesty and which was afterwards shown publicly, some months ago in London, as that horse does the meanest of the breed. Nor was his form deficient in utility. He died, I think, in 1785, at the age of nineteen years.

H. CECIL PAWSON, *ROBERT BAKEWELL*, 1957

The Horse Population

This year of the old Queen's death was almost certainly that in which the horse population of Britain reached its highest point. There is absolutely no way of proving this, because it was not in the British tradition to count numbers of horses, even though they and men and steam were the only effective source of industrial and warlike energy. There were 32,526,075 people in England and Wales this year. Between them, they owned 2,055,104 pigs, 5,534,613 cattle and 18,975,791 sheep. Horses working on farms were 1,316,538, but that was less than half the story. Adding in Scotland, Professor F.M.L. Thompson of London University has concluded that altogether there were about 3,277,000: but he left out pit-horses of which about 70,000 worked underground, and perhaps some others. The present writer also, and independently, has made a similar calculation and believes that there were possibly a few more. Both agree that 1901 represents the apogee. As no one else has ventured to bend his brain so assiduously to this task, the reader may as well accept the Professor's figure as a slight underestimate.

KEITH CHIVERS, *THE LONDON HARNESS HORSE PARADE*, 1985

Specimens of the Shire Horse

The Shire Horse, so-called from being chiefly bred in the Midland Counties, and the most powerful animal of its kind, is the descendant of the old English Great Horse, or Black Horse, which was used as a war-horse when armour was

The High Peak Shire Horse Society.

SEASON 1940.

"OLD HOUSE LINCOLN II."

42728.

Horses of this substance and quality indicate the sterling role played by the stallion hiring societies. Each stallion might beget 'a hundred mighty sons' on his rounds.

THE HIGH PEAK SHIRE HORSE SOCIETY
has hired from
E. BOSTOCK, ESQ., Gibbet Hill, Coventry,

THE SHIRE STALLION

"Old House Lincoln II."

42728.   BROWN.   Foaled 1936.   17.1 H.H.
Winner of Championship at Peterboro' in March, 1939.

Sire—**OLD HOUSE LINCOLN 41007,**
Who won 1st and Champion, Rutland, Kingston, Fennie Hunt, Melton Mowbray and Lutterworth Shows.

He sired many winners and High Priced Animals, including "Old House Miss Lincoln," sold for **310 gns.** at Peterboro' in March, 1937

g Sire—**LINCOLN WHAT'S WANTED II, 35812,**
A **London Champion** and a marvellous sire, having got the **Three times London Champion Mare,** "Lockinge Ridgway Rose," and that wonderful gelding " Pendley Warrant," also a **London Champion.**

Dam—**128355 BLUE GIRL,** a winner of prizes at several Midland Shows, standing 17.1 on clean, hard, natural legs and good feet ; by Fenny Compton Coming King, 38802, a big winner, by Harboro Nulli Secundus, a London Champion, and out of a Childwick Champion dam.

g dam—**114373 JOAN,** by Halstead Blue Blood, 37397, sold for **2,000 gns.,** and out of the great Show mare,"Halstead Duchess VII"

gg dam—**99273 MILESTONE JANET,** by King's Messenger, 31562, by **King Cole VII,** sold for **900 gns.** at a Tring Sale, and out of " Belle Cole," a **London Champion.**

ggg dam—**MILESTONE BETTY,** by Blusterer 25945, a London winner, and g sire of the dam's sire of Atterton Conquering Mimic, 1st London, 1939.

gggg dam—**MILESTONE FOREST QUEEN,** a big winner by that great breeding horse, Lockinge Forest King, 18867.

Service Fee £4 0s. 0d. net.

For payment on or before September 1st, 1940.
Ten Shillings extra will be charged for collecting fees not paid by September 1st 1940.

Any person using "Old House Lincoln II" must pay the Member's Subscription of 5/- for the current year.

Any member who is in arrears of one or more year's Subscriptions shall pay one year's Subscription of 5/- in addition to the current year's Subscription.

TERMS.

NO BUSINESS ON SUNDAYS.

Every care will be taken, but the Society will not be responsible for accidents from any cause.

All mares must arrive at sleeping places not later than 7.30 p.m., or might not be attended to.

The groom may refuse to allow trial or service of a mare if in his opinion such service would be prejudicial to the Stallion.

The route is subject to alteration by the Travelling or Management Committee.

No mare shall be served twice within 10 days unless with the consent of the groom in charge of the stallion.

All Fees and Subscriptions are due at time of service.

Any complaints should be made to the Secretary or any member of Travelling Committee :—Viz.: Ald. G. W. P. Beswick (Chairman) G. H. Drewry (Vice-Chairman), Messrs. R. Bateman, J. Davidson, J. Etches, J. T. Hall, R. Howard, S. Mellor, G. W. Morris, E. Lees, R. F. Preston, C. H. Prince, R. Thorpe and F. Whitehead.

For Nominations and Particulars apply to—
E. B. DUNN, Secretary,
Biggin Grange, Hartington, Buxton.
Telephone : Hartington 248.

worn, and was capable of carrying 32 stone. By Queen Elizabeth's time it was relegated to the duties of a coach-horse, and is now employed only as a draught-horse. In colour it is generally black, often with a white star on the forehead and white fetlocks; the tail and mane are profuse, and the legs very hairy. Although originally English, the Shire Horse was in early days crossed with Neapolitan and Flanders Horses (which have Barb blood in their veins) if not with the Barb itself, and it has been suggested that the colour of the breed is largely due to Barb ancestry. Evidence of such a crossing appears to be afforded by the presence of a distinct characteristic of Barbs, Arabs, and Thoroughbreds. In the limb-bones the rudimentary lateral digits are very strongly developed.

Among specimens of this breed exhibited in the North Hall is the skull of 'Blaisdon Conqueror.' This famous horse, whose sire was 'Hitchin Conqueror' and dam 'Welcome,' was foaled in 1894, and died in October, 1904. He stood 17 hands 2 inches in height, and was placed in the first class and won many cups and other prizes at the Shire Horse Show at Islington in 1899, 1902, and 1904. His number was 15989 in the *Shire Horse Stud Book*. The skull and limb-bones were presented by the breeder and owner, Mr P. Stubs, in 1905. The limbs of the left side are exhibited, as mentioned above, alongside those of the Thoroughbred 'Stockwell.'

In the year 1905 the Museum also received the skull of another Shire Stallion, 'Prince William', who was foaled in 1883, and died in 1905. His stud book number was 3956, and his breeder Mr W.H. Potter. The skull was presented by Lady Wantage in 1905. Both in this and the last speciment the vestige of the preorbital depression is very clearly displayed. The cannon-bones of 'Prince William' are exhibited in one of the table-cases, to show the great development of the splint-bones characteristic of this breed.

The large case in the central arch on the northern side of the hall contains the mounted head and skull of the famous Shire Mare 'Starlight,' presented in 1906 by Mrs Crisp, the widow of the owner, Mr F. Crisp, of Long Stanton, Cambridgeshire. This mare was foaled in 1882, and died in 1899, her sire being 'Sir Colin' and her dam 'Williamson's Mettle.' She was winner of a large number of first and champion prizes at various shows, and likewise took the gold medal at the London Shire Horse Show in 1890, 1891, and 1892.

R. LYDEKKER, *GUIDE TO THE SPECIMENS OF THE HORSE FAMILY (EQUIDAE)*, 1922

They Say About Horses . . .

An horse is a vain thing for safety.

PSALM xxxiii, 17

* * * * *

A horse is an animal dangerous at both ends and uncomfortable in the middle.

THE NOVICE

* * * * *

Go anywhere in England where there are natural, wholesome, contented and really nice English people; and what do you always find? That the stables are the real centre of the household.

GEORGE BERNARD SHAW, *HEARTBREAK HOUSE*

* * * * *

He doth nothing but talk of his horse.

Portia in WILLIAM SHAKESPEARE, *THE MERCHANT OF VENICE*

* * * * *

A neighing quadruped, used in wars, and draught and carriage.

SAMUEL JOHNSON, *THE DICTIONARY*

* * * * *

One white foot, buy a horse,
Two white feet, try a horse,
Three white feet, look well about him,
Four white feet, do without him.

STABLE RHYME

James Howell's Proverbs, 1659, expresses the same prejudice against four white socks:

A four white-foot horse is a horse for a fool,
A three white-foot horse is a horse for a king,
And if he hath but one I'll give him to none.

three

Shire

The Old English Breed of cart-horse was not officially named the Shire until five years after its first stud book was compiled. The Shire has become the synonym for the heavy horse in some people's eyes, and is the most numerous and widespread heavy breed in Britain.

Men of position and power took the Shire to their hearts. Two successive monarchs were great Shire breeders. Landlords vied with each other at the London Show, whose modern equivalent is the Spring Show at Peterborough, and provided top-class stallions for their home farms and, even more importantly, for

This Shire stallion, property of the Duke of Devonshire, exemplifies the quality of horse bought by landowners for their own and their tenants' benefit.

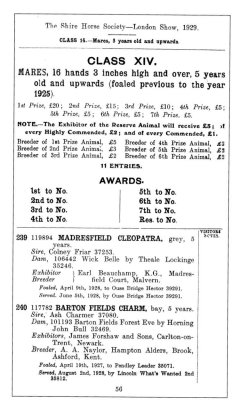

CLASS 14.—Mares, 5 years old and upwards.

CLASS XIV.

MARES, 16 hands 3 inches high and over, 5 years old and upwards (foaled previous to the year 1925).

1st Prize, £20; *2nd Prize*, £15; *3rd Prize*, £10; *4th Prize*, £5; *5th Prize*, £5; *6th Prize*, £5; *7th Prize*, £5.

NOTE.—The Exhibitor of the Reserve Animal will receive £5; of every Highly Commended, £2; and of every Commended, £1.

Breeder of 1st Prize Animal, £5   Breeder of 4th Prize Animal, £2
Breeder of 2nd Prize Animal, £3   Breeder of 5th Prize Animal, £2
Breeder of 3rd Prize Animal, £2   Breeder of 6th Prize Animal, £2

11 ENTRIES.

AWARDS.

1st to No.	5th to No.
2nd to No.	6th to No.
3rd to No.	7th to No.
4th to No.	Res. to No.

239   119894 **MADRESFIELD CLEOPATRA**, grey, 5 years.
Sire, Colney Friar 37253.
Dam, 106442 Wick Belle by Theale Lockinge 35246.
Exhibitor } Earl Beauchamp, K.G., Madres-
Breeder } field Court, Malvern.
Foaled, April 9th, 1928, to Ouse Bridge Hector 39291.
Served. June 5th, 1928, by Ouse Bridge Hector 39291.

240   117782 **BARTON FIELDS CHARM**, bay, 5 years.
Sire, Ash Charmer 37080.
Dam, 101193 Barton Fields Forest Eve by Horning John Bull 32469.
Exhibitors, James Forshaw and Sons, Carlton-on-Trent, Newark.
Breeder, A. A. Naylor, Hampton Alders, Brook, Ashford, Kent.
Foaled, April 19th, 1927, to Pendley Leader 35071.
Served, August 2nd, 1928, by Lincoln What's Wanted 2nd 35812.

56

CLASS 14.—Mares, 5 years old and upwards (*continued*).

VISITORS' NOTES.

241   88450 **ERFYL LADY GREY**, grey, 14 years.
Sire, Moors Kitchener 25443.
Dam, 88451 Erfyl Lady White by Moors Chief 22594.
Exhibitor, G. R. C. Foster, Anstey Hall, Trumpington, Cambridge.
Breeder, William Vaughan, Hafod, Llanerfyl, Welshpool, Mont.
Served, August 15th, 1928, by Bower Black Prince 39848.

242 Withdrawn.

243   113096 **SUNDORNE JOLLY 2nd**, bay, 8 years.
Sire, Sundorne It 34361.
Dam, 100385 Sundorne Jolly by Tandridge Coming King 29926.
Exhibitor, G. R. C. Foster, Anstey Hall, Trumpington, Cambridge.
Breeder, R. G. Warner, Hunkington, Withington, Shrewsbury.
Foaled, April 6th, 1928, to Bower Goalkeeper 39849.
Served, June 14th, 1928, by Medmenham Lockfast 40349.

244   118173 **FENNY MISTY MORN**, black, 5 years.
Sire, Marden Blend 36734.
Dam, 103071 Fenny Clansman's Girl by Champion's Clansman 29221.
Exhibitor, Major J. A. Morrison, D.S.O., Pendley Stock Farms, Tring, Herts.
Breeder, late George Cotterill, Fenny Compton, Leamington.
Foaled, May 21st, 1928, to Cippenham Recorder 39866.
Served, June 7th, 1928, by Seedsman 39589.

245   118409 **KERRY CLANISH MAID**, brown, 6 years.
Sire, Basildon Clansman 36277.
Dam, 108657 Kerry Blossom by Halstead Blue Blood 27397.
Exhibitor, Major J. A. Morrison, D.S.O., Pendley Stock Farms, Tring, Herts.
Breeder, Ben Alderson, Glanmeheli, Kerry, Newtown, Mont.
Foaled, April 2nd, 1928, to Seedsman 39589.
Served, May 19th, 1928, by Monks Green Friar 35891.

57

Names to conjure with. The first and second mares in this class were among the greatest ever to grace the Shire breed.

the benefit of their tenants. Timely work on the land was essential in those days before the introduction of weed spray, and the correct type of staunch, active Shire helped farmers and city hauliers alike to continue in business.

A working farmer who bred an exceptional Shire foal had a ready market from wealthy landowners. The British farmer can breed anything under the sun if there's money in it, so this potential jackpot provided a ready spur to constantly strive after improvement. One need only note the Shire exhibitors at the Royal Show, Carlisle, 1902, to appreciate how popular these animals were with the more wealthy classes of society. Shire stallions foaled in 1900 were granted seven awards from twelve entries, three absent. The winning owners were Lord Rothschild, Lord Llangattock, Earl Egerton of Tatton, James Forshaw & Sons, Henry Mackereth, Sir J.B. Maple and the Duchess of Newcastle.

Any tenant farmer who could supply that company with an outstanding Shire could make his own family's name and fortune. More than one farm has been bought from the proceeds of a single superlative animal.

Childwick Champion: over 45 per cent of Shire stallions registered in 1949 harked back in the male line to this horse. He lived from 1903 to 1924.

The long-serving breed society officials added to their routine duties by recording and discussing the breeding and management of Shires. Since the 'revival', dating from about 1970, this task fell on Keith Chivers, the late John Porter and a number of regular contributors to heavy horse and general horse magazines.

A Few Records

Reference has already been made to Harold, Premier, and Prince William, as sires, but there have been others equally famous since the Shire Horse Society has been in existence. Among them may be mentioned Bar None, who won at the 1882 London Show for the late Mr James Forshaw, stood for service at his celebrated Carlton Stud Farm for a dozen seasons, and is credited with having sired over a thousand foals. They were conspicuous for flat bone and silky feather, when round cannon bones and curly hair were much more common than they are today, therefore both males and females by Bar None were highly prized; £2000 was refused for at least one of his sons, while a two-year-old daughter made 800 guineas in 1891. For several years the two sires of Mr A.C. Duncombe, at Calwich, Harold and Premier, sired many winners, and in those days the Ashbourne Foal Show was worth a journey to see.

In 1899 Sir P. Albert Muntz took first prize in London with a big-limbed yearling, Dunsmore Jameson, who turned out to be the sire of strapping yearlings, two- and three-year-olds, which carried all before them in the show ring for several years, and a three-year-old son made the highest price ever realized at any of the Dunsmore Sales, when the stud was dispersed in 1909. This was 1025 guineas given by Lord Middleton for Dunsmore Jameson II. For four years in succession, 1903 to 1906, Dunsmore Jameson sired the highest number of winners, not only in London, but at all the principal shows. His service fee was fifteen guineas to 'approved mares only,' a high figure for a horse which had only won at the Shire Horse Show as a yearling. Among others he sired Dunsmore Raider, who in turn begot Dunsmore Chessie, Champion mare at the London Shows of 1912 and 1913. Jameson contained the blood of Lincolnshire Lad on both sides of his pedigree.

By the 1907 show another sire had come to the front, and his success was phenomenal; this was Lockinge Forest King, bred by the late Lord Wantage in 1889, purchased by the late Mr J.P. Cross, of Catthorpe Towers, Rugby, who won first prize, and reserve for the junior cup with him in London as a three-year-old, also first and champion at the (Carlisle) Royal Show the same year, 1902. It is worth while to study the breeding of Lockinge Forest King.

Sire – Lockinge Manners.
Grand sire – Prince Harold.
Great grand sire – Harold.
Great great grand sire – Lincolnshire Lad II. 1365.
Great great great grand sire – Lincolnshire Lad 1196 (Drew's).

The dam of Lockinge Forest King was The Forest Queen (by Royal Albert, 1885, a great sire in his day); she was first prize winner at the Royal Show, Nottingham, 1888, first and champion, Peterborough, 1888, first Bath and West, 1887 and 1888, and numerous other prizes. Her dam traced back to (Dack's) Matchless (1509), a horse which no less an authority than the late Mr James Forshaw described as 'the sire of all time.'

This accounts for the marvellous success of Lockinge Forest King as a stud horse, although his success, unlike Jameson's, came rather late in his life of ten years. He died in 1909. We have already seen that he has sired the highest priced Shire mare publicly sold. At the Newcastle Royal of 1908, both of the gold medal winners were by him, so were the two champions at the 1909 Shire Horse Show. His most illustrious family was bred by a tenant farmer, Mr John

Bradley, Halstead, Tilton, Leicester. The eldest member is Halstead Royal Duke, the London Champion of 1909, Halstead Blue Blood, 3rd in London, 1910, both owned by Lord Rothschild, and Halstead Royal Duchess, who won the junior cup in London for her breeder in 1912. The dam of the trio is Halstead Duchess III by Menestrel, by Hitchin Conqueror (London Champion, 1890).

Two other matrons deserve to be mentioned, as they will always shine in the history of the Shire breed. One is Lockington Beauty by Champion 457, who died at a good old age at Batsford Park, having produced Prince William, the champion referred to more than once in these pages, his sire being William the Conqueror.

To look at – I saw her in 1890 – Lockington Beauty was quite a common mare with obviously small knees, and none too much weight and width, her distinguishing feature being a mane of extraordinary length.

The remaining dam to be mentioned as a great breeder is Nellie Blacklegs by Bestwick's Prince, famous for having bred five sons – which were all serving mares in the year 1891 – and a daughter, all by Premier. The first was Northwood, a horse used long and successfully by Lord Middleton and the sire of Birdsall Darling, the dam of Birdsall Menestrel, London champion of 1904. The second, Hydrometer, first in London in 1889, then sold to the late Duke of Marlborough, and purchased when his stud was dispersed in 1893 by the Warwick Shire Horse Society for 600 guineas. Then came Chancellor, sold at Mr A.C. Duncombe's sale in 1891 for 1100 guineas, a record in those days, to Mr F. Crisp, who let him to the Peterborough Society in 1892 for £500. Calwich Topsman, another son, realized 500 guineas when sold, and Senator made 350. The daughter, rightly named 'Sensible', bred Mr John Smith of Ellastone, Ashbourne, a colt foal by Harold in 1893, which turned out to be Markeaton Royal Harold, the champion stallion of 1897. This chapter was headed 'A few records', and surely this set up by Premier and Nellie Blacklegs is one.

The prefix 'Birdsall' has been seen in show catalogues for a number of years, which mean that the animals holding it were bred, or owned, by Lord Middleton, at Birdsall, York, he being one of the first noblemen to found a stud, and he has ably filled the Presidential Chair of the Shire Horse Society. As long ago as the 1892 London Show there were two entries from Birdsall by Lord Middleton's own sire, Northwood, to which reference is made elsewhere.

Another notable sire purchased by his lordship was Menestrel, first in London, 1900 (by Hitchin Conqueror), his most famous son being Birdsall Menestrel, dam Birdsall Darling by Northwood, sold to Lord Rothschild as a yearling. As a two-year-old this colt was Cup winner and reserve Champion, and at four he was Challenge Cup winner. A good bidder at Shire sales, the breeder of a champion, and a consistent supporter of the Shire breeding industry since 1883, it is regrettable that champion honours have not fallen to Lord Middleton himself.

Among those who have done much to promote the breeding of the Old English type of cart-horse, the name of Mr Clement Keevil deserves a foremost place. At Blagdon, Malden, Surrey, he held a number of stud sales in the eighties and nineties, to which buyers went for massive-limbed Shires of the good old strains; those with a pedigree which traced back to Honest Tom (*alias* Little David), foaled in the year 1769, to Wiseman's Honest Tom, foaled in 1800, or to Samson a sire weighing 1 ton 8 cwt. Later he had a stud at Billington, Beds, where several sales were held, the last being in 1908, when Mr Everard gave 860 guineas for the stallion, Lockinge Blagdon. Shortly before that he sold Blagdon Benefactor for 1000 guineas.

J.A. FROST, *THE SHIRE HORSE IN PEACE AND WAR*, 1915

Those Magnificent Chestnuts . . .

. . . and I mean chestnut Shires, not chestnut Suffolks.

In the first *official* scale of points for the breed, drawn up by the Shire Horse Society, and printed in the *Stud Book*, volume 96 of 1972, it is stated 'a stallion should not be roan or chestnut', although these colours are reluctantly allowed for mares and geldings. However, this prejudice did not always hold. Statistics should be used carefully and briefly, but the figures show that, of the 138 stallions registered in the *Stud Book*, Volume 2 of 1881, twenty-three (16 per cent) were chestnut and of the 516 mares seventy-five (14½ per cent) were this now rather obnoxious shade. Grey, which has since been a very much accepted colour, had a much lower number – eight grey stallions (6 per cent) and forty mares (7.7 per cent).

The results at the first Shire Horse Society show held at Islington in 1880 are equally revealing as to the favourable part chestnuts played in the early days. In the five classes for stallions, three of the first prizes were won by chestnuts and two by bays. The chestnut Champion 440 won the five-year-old-and-upward class, and the second-prize winner was also chestnut. It was said of Champion 'Breeders will do well to bear him in mind, and try to breed as many like him as possible . . . He is a true type of Shire Horse.' Then there were the three-year-old Rutland Champion and the yearling Coming Wonder winning firsts; no colour prejudice here.

All through the history of these early shows we find chestnuts winning if they were good enough, and in 1884 a chestnut won the supreme female championship. This was Czarina, a three-year-old filly by the bay Helmdon Emperor out of a mare by England's Glory 745, and a contemporary report says of her 'Czarina . . . is a wonder for her age; her immense substance, depth of rib, length of quarter, flat bone, fine quality of hair, good feet, and, for so

Tiny the Shire meets Mighty the kitten. (Daniel Thwaites plc)

heavy a filly, fine action, render her an animal in every way fitted to receive honours as a champion female of the Shire breed'. She was owned by the Hon Edward Coke, of Longford Hall, Derby, president in 1881, whose foible was that the names of all his registered Shires started with the letter C.

The first twenty or so Shire shows, up to the turn of the century, usually had a few chestnuts in the prize list. In 1885 two of the six stallion classes were won by horses of this colour; Royal Sandy was first in the big stallion class, and was let for £500, and Marauder led the three-year-olds.

In 1886 Gracchus was the best four-year-old, and two stallions and three mares got second prizes, Coronet, second in the little stallion class being a full-brother to Czarina. In 1887 the first three in the little stallion class, Sir Garnet, Gracchus and Coronet, were all chestnut.

The year 1889 saw the last chestnut stallion to win a first prize at a Shire Horse Society annual show. This was the three-year-old RR 6300 by MM 3205 and he was described by Sanders Spencer, who from 1882 to 1890 wrote the official Shire Horse show reports, as handsome, stylish and free-moving.

About this time Herman Biddell, compiler of *The Suffolk Horse Stud Book*, Volume 1, gives us a very interesting although slightly sarcastic description of what a ring full of Shires would look like. 'The Shire-bred man is in no wise particular. Watching the ring at the Royal, one sees black, brown, grey, bay and chestnut; with or without white, whole coloured, blotched and sandy roan. The breeders of these fashionable horses on this point are totally without prejudice, and stopping short of sky-blue or emerald green, they apparently claim all shades as the 'true' colour of the Shire-bred proper.'

So chestnut seems to be thoroughly accepted as a Shire Horse colour, but prejudice is beginning to creep in. In the report of the class won by RR in 1889, the fourth-prize horse, the chestnut Burton King, is described by Spencer thus 'If he had been a good bay or brown he might have secured more admirers'.

Chestnuts continued to have a fair share of show successes during the nineties, with the best year being 1895. This was when the society re-introduced the gelding classes after dropping them in 1887, and also held the first gelding championship. This championship was won by the three-year-old chestnut Elford Captain. Chestnuts took the first three places in the three-year-old filly class, with Vulcan's Flower at the top and also becoming junior champion. In 1896 Flower was second in the four-year-old class to Catthorpe Naxos, the 'dark horse' of the show, and reserve senior and supreme to that mare.

Although show-yard successes were reasonably plentiful among chestnuts, we ought to take a look at stud book entries. From Volume 4 of 1883 to Volume 20 of 1899 numbers among the mares remained fairly constant at about 9 per cent. Stallions showed more fluctuation but settled in the nineties to about 6 per cent. All the best studs in the land, including that of HRH

Edward Prince of Wales at Sandringham, had chestnuts as a matter of course. The rot seemed to set in after 1900. Chestnut stallions had dropped to between 2 and 3 per cent from 1909 to 1919 and then virtually disappeared. Mares were down to 6 per cent by 1909 but faded away much more gradually. I can discover plenty of prejudice against chestnut Shires among writers of the time, but no real reason for the colour's unpopularity.

But there was a tuneful swansong to come. From 1898 to 1909 only two chestnuts, both mares, won first prizes at the annual shows. Then in 1908 a chestnut filly foal was born to the seven-year-old chestnut mare 39317 Jewel's Eve owned by J. and M. Hewitt, of Monks Kirby, near Lutterworth. This foal was by the bay Dunsmore Raider who was out of the chestnut Dunsmore Combine. Eve herself was by Harold's grandson, the chestnut Puckrup Prince Harold 18294. The chestnut foal was acquired by Sir P. Albert Muntz Bart MP, of Dunsmore, near Rugby, and christened 60183 Dunsmore Chessie. In 1911 she was London junior champion, beating the then two-year-old and later triple champion Lorna Doone, and won at many summer shows.

Dunsmore Chessie came into her own as a four-year-old in 1912, winning the Supreme Female Championship at Islington, and this despite being a chestnut. But she was a good mare, long-bodied, low to the ground but with depth, size and superlative limbs which would be allowed today. She repeated this win in 1913, and had a bay colt foal by Marden Forest King.

It might be thought that a chestnut double champion would bring a rash of that colour into the show-ring. This was not so, however, and the only discernible result of Dunsmore Chessie's wins was the number of chestnut mares after 1911 called (prefix) Chessie.

As there were no chestnut stallions about in the twenties, there ought to have been some super geldings. But even they were scarce. The chestnut Dogdyke Premier won the gelding championship in 1920 with the chestnut three-year-old Prince Reserve, and the last chestnut to win a first in London was the three-year-old gelding Punch in 1921. But in 1925 a team of chestnut Shire geldings owned by Mann, Crossman and Paulin Limited were shown in the commercial class for 'The best team of four heavy horses of the Shire type, shown without harness or vehicle, regularly worked for six months previous to date of show' and they gained reserve for silver cup for the best team.

In 1930 the *Farmer & Stockbreeder* says, in its report of the London Show, 'Chesnut (sic) has long been shunned by Shire Horse breeders, and only three of this colour were catalogued, a colt, a mare and a gelding'. And the last chestnut to appear at the Shire Horse Society Annual Show was an unnamed three-year-old gelding, by Kirkland Black Friar, who was commended in 1936. Horley Ginger 43218 in volume 61 of 1940 was the last chestnut stallion to be registered, but there was a chestnut filly 140399 Stuntney Catherine registered in volume 98 of 1974, the first since 139456 Kenwyn Lady Ann in volume 86.

So that is how the tale of the chestnuts ends, not with a bang but a whimper. However, we'll let that incomparable horseman and horse-writer, the late R.S. Summerhayes, have the last word. Writing in *Country Life*, May 1946, he says, '*No* chestnuts will be found among Shire Horses, which is a pity. To imagine a bright chestnut stallion with, perhaps, four white legs, standing in the ring on a bright summer's day is to picture something almost *too* magnificent.'

JOHN M. PORTER, HEAVY HORSE & DRIVING, 1977

Essential Quality

The yeoman breeders in maintaining the type and developing the standard points of the Shire Horse, have implanted in him their own essential qualities of courage, endurance, patience and faithful service.

Woof and warp of the fabric of our National Life, they share a common heritage as sprung from the same fertile soil of

> . . . This little world;
> This precious stone set in the silver sea,
> This blessed plot, this earth, this realm
> This England!

Of majestic size and bearing, striking action and courage.

'Each link in the chain one strength' – that is a beautifully balanced horse, one whose whole body moves in unison with great ease – and without friction, embodying all the fine points above mentioned, and attracts even people who are not horsemen.

A.B. CHARLTON, THE SHIRE HORSE SOCIETY JUBILEE HISTORY, 1928

Seeing All Three At Once

It belonged to Richard Clayton of South Carolina. He passed it to a friend, requesting him to send it to Sir John Miller, who has presented it to the Shire Horse Archive where it is now an item of peculiar interest.

Why am I excited by a slight decrepit catalogue of the Ninth Annual Shire Horse Show at the Royal Agricultural Hall, Islington? The answer lies in the date. Any old London catalogue would be very acceptable, but this one of

47

1888 contains the three stallions in whose seed lay the future of the whole breed. They were all in the same class, too!

Whoever it was that bought this catalogue and gazed at the stallions in Class I (16.2 hh and over, five years old and upwards) obviously could have had no idea that he was seeing something amazing. Nor could anyone else until at least 1940 – or perhaps even 1976, when I was fortunately able to work things out.

I will explain shortly, but first let us visit the Show ourselves, as ghosts from a future age with the benefit of hindsight. It will cost 12½p each to get in, but we can use the catalogue from South Carolina, saving 2½p. I'll tell you which horses to look out for.

No. 2, Prince William, will win the class. He was bred at Lockington in Leicestershire by W.H. Potter and is presently owned by Lord Wantage, who was awarded the VC in the Crimean War. In 1854 he was young Robert Lloyd-Lindsay, only twenty-two.

Hitchin Conqueror, No. 5, is the same age (five) and by the same sire, William the Conqueror. He was bred by Potter's neighbour George Shepperson and belongs to A.B. Freeman-Mitford, more familiar to us of course as Lord Redesdale, grandfather of our own Duchess of Devonshire and the other 'Mitford Girls'. This horse will be highly commended.

No. 17 is Harold, seven years old and bred by another of the Potters – J.H. of Spondon about 6 miles from W.H., but in Derbyshire. Now the property of A.C. Duncombe of Calwich Abbey, he'll stand fifth, just missing a prize.

Remarkable

There! You've seen them together for the only possible time, and without shifting your position in time or space. And isn't it remarkable that two were born at Lockington, a parish of about 450 souls? (Two and two are three). Three horses with two sires.

Pedigrees

Now the Show is over, I must explain about the three stallions I especially asked you to see. Let us return to the Hall a third of a century later (1921), come home again and study the pedigrees of all 132 stallions and mares that win awards. We shall discover that 91 of them are directly descended in the male line from Lincolnshire Lad II (86 via his son Harold) and 40 from William the Conqueror via Hitchin Conqueror (31) and Prince William (9). The odd one out is a descendant of Premier who was owned , like Harold, by Mr Duncombe.

If we move another 18 years to 1939, we shall find this dominance is complete – not just in the unreal world of shows, but in breeding the whole race of Shire cart horses. The number of stallions accepted that year for inclusion in the 1940 volume of the *Stud Book* was 238. Of these, Harold was the male-line

CLASS 2.—Stallions, 2 years old (*continued*).

VISITORS' NOTES.

39 BROCKHILL MIRACLE 40224, brown, 2 years.
Sire, Pendley Record 35951.
Dam, 107253 Brockhill Betty by Marden John 32580.
Exhibitor, Sir Walter Gilbey, Bart., The Lodge, Elsenham, Essex.
Breeder, H. S. Thomas, Henwick Manor, Newbury.
FOR SALE by AUCTION on THURSDAY.

40 Withdrawn.

41 TILTON HIAWATHA 40440, bay, 2 years.
Sire, Woolscott King Cole 39073.
Dam, 83247 Tilton Jenny by Tatton Dray King 23777.
Exhibitor, Sir Walter Gilbey, Bart., The Lodge, Elsenham, Essex.
Breeder, Allan Holm, Tilton, Leicester.
FOR SALE by AUCTION on THURSDAY.

42 MARDEN UMPIRE 40340, bay, 2 years.
Sire, Cowage Dalesman 39149.
Dam, 104750 Northlands Belle 2nd by Champion's Goalkeeper 30296.
Exhibitor) Sir Bernard Greenwell, Bart., Marden
Breeder) Park, Woldingham, Surrey.

43 MARDEN UNIONIST 40341, black, 2 years.
Sire, Cowage Dalesman 39149.
Dam, 94331 Marden Rosalind by Champion's Goalkeeper 30296.
Exhibitor) Sir Bernard Greenwell, Bart., Marden
Breeder) Park, Woldingham, Surrey.

44 MAIDENCOURT HEIRLOOM 40330, bay, 2 years.
Sire, Heirloom 3rd 39510.
Dam, 114765 Maidencourt Mollie by Leadenham Menestrel 2nd 35788.
Exhibitor) H. T. Hincks, Keyham Hall,
Breeder) Leicester.

45 EDINGALE BLEND 40272, brown, 2 years.
Sire, Hawton Blend 38845.
Dam, 112671 Queen's Farm Gem by Harboro' Nulli Secundus 33231.
Exhibitor) E. J. Holland, Edingale House, Tam-
Breeder) worth.
[For Sale Privately.]
10

CLASS 2.—Stallions, 2 years old (*continued*).

VISITORS' NOTES.

46 SEVERN PLANTER 40394, brown, 2 years.
Sire, Seedsman 39589.
Dam, 102801 Dove Farm Duchess by Champion's Clansman 29221.
Exhibitor, Norman R. Lloyd, Walcot, Chirbury, Salop.
Breeder, William Sargeant, Dove Farm, Ellastone, Derbyshire.

47 PENDLEY HARVESTER 40368, black, 2 years.
Sire, Seedsman 39589.
Dam, 99582 Pendley Lady by Champion's Goalkeeper 30296.
Exhibitor, Major J. A. Morrison, D.S.O., Pendley Stock Farms, Tring, Herts.
Breeders, A. Hall and Sons, The Manor, Towton, Tadcaster.
[For Sale Privately.]

48 PINCHBECK FRIAR CHAMPION (Vol. 51), brown, 2 years.
Sire, Cippenham Friar 38110.
Dam, 99642 Pinchbeck Queen's Messenger by King's Messenger 31562.
Exhibitors, F. W. Parsons and Sons, Speckington, Ilchester, Somerset.
Breeder, J. T. Holmes, Stud Farm, Pinchbeck, Spalding.
FOR SALE by AUCTION on THURSDAY.

49 SNELSTON REAPER 40402, brown, 2 years.
Sire, Seedsman 39589.
Dam, 96624 Alsager Princess Royal by Champion's Goalkeeper 30296.
Exhibitor, Mrs. Stanton, Snelston Hall, Ashbourne.
Breeder, A. Colclough, Hassall House, Sandbach, Cheshire.

50 FANCOURT PRINCE 40278, bay, 2 years.
Sire, Pendley Candidate 39293.
Dam, 99586 Pendley Princess 4th by Norbury Menestrel 23543.
Exhibitor) Sir Edward D. Stern, Bart., Fan
Breeder) Court, Chertsey, Surrey.
11

An extract from *The Shire Horse Society – London Show, 1929*, showing entrants in Class 2 – Stallions, 2 years old.

ancestor of 217, Hitchin Conqueror of 18 and Prince William of three. No others.

Whether the Harold blood-line in due course would have completely eliminated that of William the Conqueror's two chief sons, and how long this would have taken, is anyone's guess. The extinction of the draught horse as a viable source of locomotive power following the Second World War enticed some people to play pedigree tricks involving the Clydesdale blood. It is unsafe to trust the *Stud Book* from then until the introduction of compulsory blood-typing. For the historian, the damage was irreparable.

Any horse now which is genuinely descended in the male line from either of William the Conqueror's two sons can claim as his ancestor John Bull, alias Fisher's Black Horse of Weston, foaled in the early 1790s – perhaps 1794. Likewise a true descendant of Harold goes back to Milton and Colley's Brown Horse of Bassingham, an exact contemporary. But who knows now?

KEITH CHIVERS, *HEAVY HORSE WORLD*, 1994

Feathery Legs

The old century was in its last year when a foal was born that was to change Shire horse fashions for half a century, and whose attributes are still harked back to in the 1980s.

Lockinge Forest King was of impeccable lineage. He also had substance and character but, above all, hair. The hair or feather on his fore legs sprouted at the black knees, and from only just below the hock on his snowy white hind legs. Not only was he thus endowed, but he passed on the same hairy attributes, which was why he had many descendants. In the early 1900s a heavily feathered Shire sold for more than a fine-haired one, and today's comparatively silky haired horses would have been laughed to scorn by Edwardian horsemen.

'The British stockbreeder can breed anything in the world if there's money in it.' When the demand was there, Swaledale sheep breeders transformed their flocks from grey faces to jet black and the legs from white to mottled, in a few generations. Pig breeders produced incredibly long, lean baconers, cattle breeders a tight udder that withstood machine milking. And all because it paid.

A Shire with hairy legs certainly paid in those pre-1914 days when grooms were plentiful and cheap, hard work a virtue and hair was equated with bone. Lockinge Forest King provided hair in such profusion that the highly skilled grooms of the period could enhance a good leg with it, and disguise a poor one.

Chivers pointed out that the horses would look very different if they were walked through a pond before sale, but they were not. They were paraded, all brushed out and dry, and doctored with resin and other noxious substances that gave the impression of masculinity, but affected the genes not at all.

The reason that Lockinge Forest King was so prepotent for hair becomes apparent in studying photographs of his ancestors. His great-grandsire was Lincolnshire Lad, whose son the grey Lincolnshire Lad II had masses of hair high up his legs. The bay Lockinge Forest King was bred by Lady Wantage at Lockinge, and later owned by J.P. Cross, Catthorpe Towers, Rugby and then by W.T. Everard, of Bardon Hall, Leicester. He won a string of notable prizes, and begat offspring that won cups and rosettes by the score. More important, the male descendants of this great stallion sired foals that sold at well above the average then obtaining, making it a business proposition for farmers to pay a handsome stud fee for their services, and therefore for the stallion owners to vie with each other in obtaining Lockinge Forest King sons and grandsons.

EDWARD HART, *THE BOOK OF THE HEAVY HORSE*, 1986

Notable Stallions

A feature of the Shire scene from the outbreak of the Second World War until the slaughter of the late 1940s was the succession of notable grey stallions. They made up over one third, 77 out of 211, registrations in the 1944 *Stud Book*, which incidentally included four roans. In 1948 the two-year-olds at the Derby Shire Horse Society Show included three greys among the six two-year-old stallion prize winners, two among nine three-year-old top stallions, three of the best seven four-year-olds, and four out of nine winning senior stallions.

Of the eight pairs of heavy horses of Shire type at the 1948 Spring Show, three pairs were greys, including the dapple greys Manea Duke and Manea Prince from G.C. Bedford. A portent was to be found in the fours, both entries being all blacks. Young & Co's Brewery Ltd and Francis L. Bowley were the stalwarts giving the crowds a revival of memories after five years of war and shortages.

The decade following peace in 1945 is a rather neglected period in Shire history. Though the breed was in numerical decline, there was still much activity among the top studs and some excellent horses in evidence. Notable among these was The Bomber, who won the 1949 Derby Show (then the chief Shire event) for Dick Sutton.

The Bomber combined the best of the old and modern types. A brown with three white legs and the off-fore black, he stood 17.2 hands high, and presented himself perfectly. He was bought in Crewe by R.G. Thompson as a three-year-old, for 650 guineas, having been bred by J. Kirkland at Belper, Derbyshire. He was used in Lancashire for two seasons, was bought by Dick Sutton and let to the Uttoxeter Society before serving mares on Anglesey. At the time there were three heavy horse societies on the island.

At that 1949 show The Bomber was eight years old. 'One of the greatest Shire stallions ever' is Herbert Sutton's recollection. He 'travelled' the stallion, not by walking, but by using a motor wagon, returning to stables each evening and setting off with a fresh horse next morning. Even in 1951–2, Suttons' stallions were covering 200 mares a season. Most stallion hiring societies continued to operate until about 1955.

One of the most important post-Second World War sales took place when Freshneys dispersed their stud. Dick Sutton bought the stallions Bengie and Great Hope for 685 and 640 guineas, quite a lot of money then. Our William went to Balderstones and Cumbers (later to found the Royal Show John Cumber Park) acquired Our Surprise for over 600 guineas.

All these horses were by Raans Record Ways, son of Raans Record. They included Woburn Dustman, who went to Suttons for 120 guineas and did as well as his more expensive brethren. As an old horse, Dustman was travelled in

A Palace of Westminster security officer checks
Young's horses making the first real ale delivery
to the House of Commons for nearly thirty
years in 1991. (Young & Co.'s Brewery plc)

Eady Robinson, holding the horse.

Lancashire by R.G. Thompson of Blackpool. He was foaled in 1938 at Woburn Abbey where the Duke of Bedford's stud was stabled. Dustman had three white legs and a white patch on his body, so not all white patches on Shires can be blamed on Clydesdale imports of the 1960s! Raans Record, incidentally, takes us another big jump back to 1929, where this brown horse with the broad stripe down his face, and four white legs, was bred by William Clark at Raans Farm, Amersham, Buckinghamshire, winning prizes as a foal.

Bengie's 685 guineas' cost was recouped when he was hired to the Uttoxeter Shire Horse Society for three seasons at 600 guineas a season. This was followed by two years with the Welshpool and one with the Fylde Societies. Great Hope went to Crewe, at over 500 guineas the season.

A horse that left a lot of winners in the early 1950s was Polwarth Spellbinder. He headed the two-year-old stallions at Peterborough in 1960. Herbert Sutton, who travelled him, said: 'Spellbinder would have done well today. He was a "modern" horse, with clean limbs and fine hair. He was hired from Bob Fish of Scotton, Lincolnshire, and I handled him for my uncle, Dick Sutton.'

A black that John Richardson tried unsuccessfully to buy was Preston King Cole. He was by Edingale What's Wanted and was hired to Welshpool in 1953. He also served mares for the Brigg, Lincolnshire, Society.

Terms for Dick Sutton's Preston Shire Stud stallions in 1953 were £4 10s for each mare. Clients requiring a stallion other than on his normal route were charged 10s extra and mares barren from the 1952 season (to Sutton's horses) had their fees reduced to £2 10s. The groom's fee was 5s, to be paid at time of service, though for many years the groom's fee had been half a crown.

In 1953 the Preston stud listed twenty-six stallions, in addition to those hired to societies, so heavy breed stallions were still big business. There is a sad little obituary to The Bomber; 'Top Stud Horse in England when he died'.

Althorpe Trump Card triumphed at Derby in 1947 and 1948. He was shown by those Shire stalwarts J. & W. Whewell, probably best remembered through Heaton Majestic, six times champion gelding in the dark days of the 1960s. The grey Crimwell Quality was female champion in the three years 1948–50.

EDWARD HART, 1986

Eady Robinson: An Appreciation

Eady Robinson, who died on 18 August, was an articulate man, but not a talkative one, and he talked least about himself. Everyone knew him. Few knew him well. Transparent men are often hollow, and he was neither.

His deep Shire wisdom stemmed partly from inborn flair. That is obvious. Without it, no horseman reaches his eminence. (His father, incidentally, joined the Shire Horse Society in 1890.)

To flair, he added experience gained in a hard school, for he was only seventeen when he had to begin fending for himself – and that was over sixty years ago.

The family had not long moved from Lillingstone Hall near Buckingham to Higham Ferrers where he remained the rest of his life. He tackled the problem of survival on a bike, cycling twenty miles and more a day – looking at horses, buying, learning his lessons. He furthered his education by visits to the Elephant and Castle horse repository, where anyone without wits and horse sense would soon go broke.

At the age of twenty-one, he was invited to judge Buckingham Foal Show with the great Tom Fowler.

'Have you ever judged before, boy? No? Well, you can do it all, and I'll sit in the middle. I can make changes when you've finished.'

Eady, trembling, said he could not agree to that unless he had an equal say at the end as well.

'Well done, boy. That's what I hoped you'd say.'

As it happened, they thought alike, and Tom took the young man to the White Hart to instruct him what, and how little, he should drink in Shire company.

First elected to the Shire Council in 1935, next year he became the youngest London Show judge of all time. He judged the Shire Show six more times, including the centenary year when, really, he should not have gone, for the accident which hastened his death made it a burden. Few realised this, because he was still the lean and dapper young man of half a century ago.

In his ability to spot a foal at the tenderest age, he rivalled another of his mentors, Harry Bishop, of Pendley. Like Bishop, too, he was equally at home judging light horses, cattle, sheep – or anything on four legs.

There was a third similarity. Neither man liked to exhibit a horse unless he thought it would win. There are some for whom second best is no good at all.

Shire men know of his outstanding animals, and a long list would not help anyone else. So I will mention only six.

Lillingstone What's Wanted won the Shire championship in 1946, Lillingstone's Brandmark in 1951 and Lillingstone's Lakes Superior in 1958–60. Of his mares, Lillingstone's Superiority was the Royal champion in 1948, Lillingstone's Lucky Chance was the 1959 Spring Show champion (so he achieved the rare double that year) and Lillingstone Again was the first ever Shire Horse of the Year in 1974.

Brandmark, which in 1948 helped him to a Royal double, was bred by that gifted son and grandson of Shire grand masters, Tom Freshney, his father-in-law.

I have one special memory of Eady – at Kenilworth in 1971, laconically, but brilliantly, describing and demonstrating the art of judging before a large audience of American and English breeders.

May England continue to produce horsemen, as it always has, of his calibre.

KEITH CHIVERS, *HEAVY HORSE & DRIVING*, 1977

The Heaton Stud

One rather raw day in 1973, I went to a horse sale at a venue with an unlikely sounding name. It was New Bridge Chemical Works, Radcliffe, right in Lancashire's industrial heart. But the stud owners, J. & W. Whewell, were known wherever Shires were bred, their prefix Heaton was among the greats, and their stud groom Reg Nunn became a legend in his own lifetime.

In view of the Shire market in the preceding decade, there seemed an inordinate number of potential buyers at that sale. Or were they summoned, as to a wake, by mere inquisitiveness and the passing of a tradition?

The prices soon proved otherwise. I wish I could pin-point that sale as the turning point and say that I was struck by a Sherlock Holmes-type of insight that made the way ahead bright and clear. Alas, at the time it seemed no more than an encouraging flash in the pan. But it was a great sale.

The highlight was, of course, Heaton Majestic. Six times had he paraded at Peterborough in the gelding class, and six times had Reg Nunn walked up for the championship cup, the massive Majestic towering above him. There was not another gelding in the country even to approach Heaton Majestic.

The horse's sire was Crossfields Supreme, and his breeder J.B. Cooke, who later bred the Golden Guinea award winner Jim's Lucky Charm. The bay mare Lucky Charm was sired by Hillmoor Enterprise, out of a Lymm Sovereign mare, Jim's Chelsea. But as is the way with pedigrees, we are straying from our theme.

The Shire Horse Society held 25 gelding championships from 1948 to Whewell's last outing, in which time the Heaton stud took sixteen of them. From 1961 to Heaton Majestic's last appearance in 1972, the stud proved unbeatable, taking all 12.

Nor should anyone think that the competition was poor. Total Peterborough entries were rising slowly, but even in 1971 Heaton Majestic paraded in a strong class of 14 including the runner-up, Coward's St Vincent's Flash Lad, plus Harry Chambers' Swanland Dale Supreme, three brewery horses from Youngs and one from Courage's. Hull Brewery also entered Noble, and Arthur Wright from Warrington with the four-year-old Ned could never be discounted.

EDWARD HART, *SHIRE HORSES*, 1983

The diminutive Reg Nunn peering up at the champion gelding Heaton Majestic. Man and horse were among the greatest of all time.

Mid-Twentieth Century

There is a strong temptation to skip heavy horse history in the late 1950s and throughout the 1960s. Homage is due to those stalwarts who carried the tattered flag, however, and there are horses of note whose blood has figured strongly in the resurrection. The last hardbacked *Shire Horse Society Stud Book* was the combined Volume 1957–9. Then came the loose leaf era; no photographs, no lists of winners, no officials' or judges' names, in fact just the bare registrations.

They were bare indeed; the five volumes 82 to 86, clipped narrowly together, contain less than a hundred stallion names. Winners return in 1963, augmented by photographs in 1964, when S.G. Garrett's Carr Coming King was champion and a yearling stallion named Ladbrook What's Wanted foretold his future for Arthur Lewis. In 1965 Carr Coming King stood second among the five senior stallions to the champion, John Suckley's Alneland Delegate, a brown showing indications of Clydesdale breeding. But no matter; he was a grand stud horse. In that year the 17 in-hand geldings numbered one more than the combined numbers of yearlings and two-year-old fillies. Today the number of geldings has fallen disproportionately low.

By 1966 names familiar in modern pedigrees appeared; Grange Wood Clifford and Grange Wood William, Edingale Draughtsman, with Grange Wood Bengie as reserve to the champion stallion, Ladbrook What's Wanted. In 1967 only twenty-eight stallions were registered but they included the grey Alneland Masterpiece, the bay Bellasize Select, Hainton Warrant, and Jim's Chieftain who set the seal on American revival when bought by Arlin Wareing, Blackfoot, Idaho. Young's showed an eight and Courage, Barclay and Simonds a six.

Even in 1970 only thirty-three Shire stallions were registered. Not till 1973 do they indicate a firmer footing, with seventy-seven registered. By 1981 eighty-eight colt foals were notified in addition to the fifty stallions registered.

In the *Preston Guardian* during the 1943 season, that great heavy horse journalist Harry Holderness described the four-year-old champion Tabley Grey Duke 43496, by Powisland Bulwark out of Pilsdon Beauty:

> He is a flash horse from whatever angle he is viewed, and his compactness and his close linking deceive one as to his height, but he is 17.1 hands for all that. Hard and steel-girdered, he is finished in the height of Shire fashion, and is wonderfully clean in his limbs, just as the champion of today ought to be. Further, he is beautifully topped and powerfully jointed.

Whewells again won the championship at Derby, under the auspices of the Shire Horse Society. Their horse was Bradford Diagram 43150, a six-year-old bay by Bradford Monogram. The bay Monogram was bred across the Pennines at Bradford by E. Patchett, and had three white legs and the near hind black. Diagram's dam was Margaret of Chippinghurst, who rose to fame rapidly as the only yearling filly to win the supreme female championship at the Shire Horse Show.

Harry Holderness wrote of Monogram in 1942:

> A stalwart, carty horse which looks like being a getter of the deep draughter type, he is essentially modern in outline, and has a general balance and grandeur of outline which is most attractive. He is white socked, deep in front, set on frontal columns of infinite strength, not too long in the back, is sufficiently deep, and has a pair of levers which betoken his power. A notable feature is the remarkable flatness of his bone. Rippling with muscles of cable strength, he has an airy grace in his locomotion that is fascinating to behold in so heavy a horse. When he goes he seems to skim the turf, the while revealing the notable size of his mallet-like hoofs.

Whewells did not achieve prominence through picking up unconsidered trifles. They bought the best, and advised others to do so. The Heaton Stud booklet reads: 'Students of pedigree should analyse the breeding of a stallion whose maternal lineage stands unsurpassed. Experimenting with chance-bred sires is a waste of time.'

The old stallion Pendley Harvester is the subject of this discourse in the booklet. He was foaled in 1927, and that year gained firsts at the leading Yorkshire shows, Wetherby, Malton, Withernsea, Church Fenton, Harrogate and Sherburn-in-Elmet, following up this early promise by leading his class in London as a yearling.

Another appreciative comment comes from Harry Holderness in 1942:

Pendley Harvester is undoubtedly a grand old gentleman and when he came out for his photograph looked amazingly fit for his advancing years. He showed off his paces to perfection, like the gallant veteran he is. He looks an old horse, of course, but he has preserved his virility to a surprising extent. He was first used when he was four years old, and has served more than a hundred mares a year since, leaving a high percentage in foal.

Pendley Harvester was a black with three white legs. He was bought by Whewells at the 1936 Pendley Stud sale for 380 guineas, or more than a hundred times the average farm man's weekly wage.

Another horse to cost the firm 380 guineas, though in 1942, was The Proctor 43672:

A sturdy bay with a blaze and three white legs, he is well grown for his age, and is noteworthy for the fine quality of his flat bone and for the really tremendous size of his foundations. His hair is in the right places and it is light and silky. There is ample heart room about him and he has that short back which is the prerequisite of the good stallion. Taken all round he looks a typical gelding getter of the Heaton type. [Written in 1943.]

And as the only true purpose of all Shire stallions is to get geldings of the Heaton type, these words are worth studying in depth.

EDWARD HART, 1983

four

Clydesdale

The Scottish equivalent of the Shire is the Clydesdale. Both breeds undoubtedly have some common origin. Around the turn of the century they drew apart, but in the dark days of the 1960s they became so similar that only a specialist could identify each, and still be wrong. In more recent times the two breeds have again separated in type and colour, only for the Scottish heavy horse to throw open its register to other breeds. The future is unclear. One factor remains constant; the horses have more similarities than the men who breed them.

The export market to North America and Australia has been so brisk that some fear the loss of too much top blood abroad. On the other hand, a booming export trade leads to mares being bred from, which might be rested in times of depression. More Clydesdales are appearing in the south of England, and are particularly popular in turnout teams and for ploughing matches.

Ann Jones from Leicestershire ploughs with a pair of light roan Clydesdales, Bonny and Clyde. Her father, Harry Tomlin, has ploughed for England. Champion ploughman Jim Elliott ploughs with Clydesdales, one of which 'just creeps along the furrow' during the finish, and much gold would be needed to buy him.

The Clydesdale has been at the forefront on several counts. Ploughing matches spread rapidly in Scotland following the introduction of a plough light enough to be drawn by a pair, rather than four or more. Breed characteristics were 'fixed' over a period of sixty years up to about 1920. The stallion hiring system north of the Border brought quality Clydesdale entires within range of most breeders, as the stud cards in this chapter show.

While English farm journals tried to cover all heavy breeds, *The Scottish Farmer* concentrated on Clydesdales. The fine quality paper used in the magazine and its almanacs brought out the best in words and pictures concerning the Clydesdale breed.

All Fire and Feather

In the 1991 Radio 4 *Brain of Britain* final, a question was asked 'Which breed of heavy horse originated in Lanarkshire by crossing imported Flemish stallions

An extract from the 1885 service diary for the Clydesdale stallion Lord Seaham, who travelled in Cumbria. He was bred by the Marquis of Londonderry at Seaham Harbour, Sunderland, in 1879, and was a bay with three white legs. David Little bought him, and used him at least until 1893. Other livestock entries in the same neat hand indicate the owner's writing, and the diary was probably made up from the groom's records. The stallion's ancestry traces directly to Volume I of the *Stud Book*.

on the native stock?' The first reply was 'Percheron'. The second, 'Clydesdale', gained marked applause when it was pronounced correct.

Such reaction is an indication that, despite the heavy horse's rising popularity, there is still a long way to go before the big ones are again part of everyday life. The Shire long since ceased to be a rare breed, but the Clydesdale has many fewer breeders and animals.

Today's Clydesdale is an upstanding, active and fast walking horse. It is little used on the land, but is an excellent exhibition horse commanding a booming export market, is sought by foresters, and is once more spreading into England.

Old Name from the County

Clydesdale was the old name for the county of Lanarkshire, where the breed

The Clydesdale stallion Benefactor, sold for 4,400 guineas as a three-year-old in 1925. The Head Photographer of *The Scottish Farmer*, John Fraser, rates this the best photograph ever taken of a heavy horse. Every aspect shows to full advantage.

originated. The heavy, cumbersome horses of the lowlands and marshes of western Europe played a part in its make-up, as they did in that of the Shires. The fact remains that these imports, which later included Shires, stamped more weight onto a very sound native horse, short in the leg and clean, well able to carry a man at an active gait.

An eighteenth-century Duke of Hamilton is credited with importing six black Flemish stallions, though not all agree. Aiton of Strathaven claimed in 1810 to have lived for many years in the district, and made all possible enquiry into the fact, but no person had heard of such stallions. Less doubt is cast about a Flemish entire imported by John Paterson, Lochlyoch, between 1715 and 1720.

Ure wrote: 'They are drawn more surely, and are better for heavy work in the field, than any other. It may, without exaggeration, be asserted that no place in Europe can turn out better horses, for the draught, than Lanarkshire'.

Need for them was enhanced through a blacksmith's skills. Small's iron swing or wheelless plough superseded the old 'twal owsen' heavy wooden

PEDIGREE :

HAWKRIGG FLASHPRINT (23399), bay, foaled 28th April, 1936. Bred by Robert Sayer, Mount Clifton, Penrith.

Sire—Dunure Flashprint (21874).

1st dam—Breaks Hall Rose (57781) by Apukwa (14567).

2nd dam—Monobel (51692) by Dunure Independence (18706).

3rd dam—Imogene (30748) by Baronson (10981).

4th dam—Chester Princess (16371) by Baron's Pride (9122).

5th dam—Orphan Princess (13281) by Prince of Fashion.

6th dam—Princess II. (10556) by Darnley (222).

7th dam—Princess of Girvan (4661) by Lord Lyon (489).

8th dam—Louise (538) by Prince of Wales (673)

A glance at the above pedigree will show "Hawkrigg Flashprint" to be one of the best bred Stallions in the Stud Book, every sire in his pedigree having been noted good breeders in their time. His fourth dam, "Chester Princess," winner of the Cawdor Cup in 1907 was considered to be one of the best mares the breed has ever produced.

"Dunure Flashprint" was a well known good breeding horse in Cumberland. "Apukwa" was a great breeding sire and was always near the top of the list of sires of prizewinners. He in turn was sired by "Hiawatha," winner of the Cawdor Cup four times in succession. "Dunure Independence" was sold at public auction for 4,900 gns., and was sired by the £9,500 horse "Baron of Buchlyvie."

"Baronson" was also the sire of the Cawdor Cup winner "Oyama." "Baron's Pride" was the great breeding horse of his day, and his stock dominated the showyards for many years. No fewer than 9 of his daughters won the "Cawdor Cup," and 7 of his daughters were dams of winners of that trophy.

The last three sires in the pedigree of "Hawkrigg Flashprint," viz. "Darnley," "Lord Lyon" and "Prince of Wales," were the great foundation sires of the Clydesdale Breed.

"Hawkrigg Flashprint's" illustrious lineage should ensure him being a most impressive sire and he is himself a nice thick weighty young horse, with a splendid outlook, feet and legs of the best quality and he moves with great style and freedom.

STATIONS :

Monday Nights—Mr. Hird's, Parkhead, Caldbeck.

Tuesday Nights—Mr. Harrison's, Low Hall.

Wednesday Nights—Hesket-New-Market.

Thursday Nights—Mr. Davis', Ruthwaite.

Friday Nights—Mr. Litt's, Whitrigg, Torpenhow.

Weekends—Hawkrigg House.

HAWKRIGG STUD HORSES,
The Highland Show Winner,
HAWKRIGG ELDORADO (22138)
Terms—£3 and £4.
Also the Kilpatrick Shield Winner,
HAWKRIGG MARQUIS (23173)
Terms—£5 and £5.
Mares Kept at Reasonable Rates.

Details from the stud card of Hawkrigg Flashprint (23399), a Clydesdale stallion owned by James Kilpatrick of Wigton, 1939.

plough, which required a picturesque but hopelessly uneconomic team of four men and boys and eight to twelve oxen.

By 1791 all forty ploughs in an Alloa ploughing match were of Small's design, invented some twenty years previously. Two horses and the ploughman sufficed. This was real progress, further stimulated by the formation of ploughing societies, whose matches became an important feature of the rural calendar.

Farming Prospered

Farming in general prospered from Queen Victoria's accession in 1837 to the mid 1870s, though Scottish workers gained little recompense. Their hard lives were enlivened each spring by the arrival of the travelling stallions, Clydesdales all. Debates on the points of the great entires were as intense as those on today's pop stars, and far more useful. Symon wrote: 'The sight of a well-matched, well-groomed, spirited pair of Clydesdales in shining harness was most pleasing to the eye. Travelling stallions were sent from the Clyde valley to all parts of Scotland.'

All this took place before the Clydesdale Horse Society of Great Britain and Ireland was formed in 1877. It was an extension of the invaluable work of the Glasgow Agricultural Society, which organized a central hiring fair to replace local ones. Keith Chivers in *The Shire Horse* tells us that by 1872 the Stallion Show was well organized and overflowing from the cattle market.

Chivers makes the point that the Highland and Agricultural Society of Scotland did more for heavy horse breeding than the English Royal. It played no small part in encouraging better horse-drawn implements as well as better horses.

Exports boomed between the *Stud Book*'s inception and the outbreak of the First World War. The 1912 volume lists 699 stallions, and almost twice that number of Clydesdales were exported in the year.

Stud Books for 1919, 1920 and 1921 have a combined width of nearly seven inches, and contain new registrations of 700 stallions and 5,000 mares. The early 1920s mark the zenith of the heavy horse, and the end of an era of fairly intense line and inbreeding among Clydesdales.

Sir Dighton was sold for 850 guineas at Mr Taylor's Park Mains sale, Renfrewshire, in 1912. He was a mousey colour, and travelled in the Biggar and Peebles districts of southern Scotland. At one ploughing match with over thirty pairs, almost every team had a Sir Dighton offspring.

Famous Sires

Famous sires include Prince of Wales 673, foaled in 1866; Darnley in 1872; his son Top Gallant who sired Sir Everard who weighed 21 cwt. in working condition while standing no more than 17.1 hands, and was the grandson of both Darnley and Prince of Wales. A Darnley granddaughter, Forest Queen, foaled Baron's Pride to Sir Everard in 1890. Champion on his only outing, 11 of Baron's Pride's offspring won the coveted Cawdor Cup. His son, Baron of Buchlyvie, replaced him as Scotland's top breeding horse, and sired six Cawdor Cup winners. Sadly, the Baron was kicked by a mare and had to be put down. His skeleton is on display in the Glasgow Museum, and worth a visit by any heavy horse lover. It shows the ideal structure of a draught horse.

Then came Dunure Footprint, 1908–30. At his peak his stud fee was £60.00, doubled when the mare was in-foal. He is credited with serving 300 mares a season. The late Richard Mitchell was a friend of Footprint's groom, and told me how, after every mare, the great horse spreadeagled on the floor of his box until the next mare arrived two hours later, round the clock.

Richard Mitchell no longer takes his customary seat in the Royal Highland grandstand. He was a great student of the breed with which he had spent his entire working life and, when I was fortunate enough to find a batch of sepia postcards depicting Clydesdale stallions, he itemized the records of every one. 'Not a good breeding stallion . . . his offspring were wild . . . never heard of after that show . . . etc'.

One point Richard Mitchell made was that Clydesdales were more sensible before the period of intensive inbreeding. 'You could teach them more easily in the early 1900s. They were calmer, more intelligent, even though they lacked the show points'.

All modern Clydesdales are said to be traceable to Dunure Footprint, who had a large light splatch on his nearside, and after becoming famous was always photographed with his head to the right!

The roan Clydesdales of the 1960s and 1970s are probably due to him. Today's favourites are bright bays (selling well in North America). Blue roans and strawberry roans are attractive – there is much to be said for distinctive breed colours, and roan stallions are barred among Shires.

Today's Spectacular

Dr Christine Wallace Mann drives a four-in-hand of chestnut Clydesdales and, though the colour is not officially encouraged, will doubtless have a chestnut 'six' storming round the ring when she can find them. Hugh Ramsey has some glorious roans in his hitch, while Tom Brewster favours bays. His gelding, Ben, was a bright bay. His premature death ended the career of one of the best harness horses on the modern show circuit.

Allan Henry breeds his own, mostly bays, in Northumberland, while no big show is complete without Mervyn Ramage and his tall roans Blue Print and Lenzie Jim.

The Scottish breed is again challenging the English, and at the 1991 East of England Show, Hugh Ramsay's Clydesdales turnout won both the 'fours' and the 'threes' in the very heart land of English Shiredom.

Clydesdales prove economic in Aberdeen parks. The 'Oil City' has pioneered a return of the draught horse for short hauls, engendering an antidote to the aggressive motor. From Hertfordshire, M. & K. Grayson show Loch Creran John, a grey Clydesdale foaled in 1985.

The far north of Scotland is seeing a big Clydesdale revival. At the Black Isle and Muir of Ord shows, entries have risen considerably, while Society membership and registrations both indicate hope for the future.

In a recent volume, number 90, of the *Stud Book*, 185 foals were registered, 63 of them colts and 122 fillies. There were nine new stallion entries, and a number of late registrations. The *Stud Book* is to be closed, unless 1992 EC regulations insist on a grading up register. And Will H. Ogilvie's words still ring true:

> Through the misty northern weather
> Stepping two and two together
> All fire and feather
> Come the Clydes!

EDWARD HART, *THE ARK*, MARCH 1992

The Best Black Horse

According to Thomas Dykes in his article on 'Clydesdale Memories' (*Trans. of Highland Agric. soc.*, 1907) horses bred by Bakewell made their contribution to the development of the heavier type of Clydesdale farm horse. Bakewell, not content with selling stallions into Scotland to the Duke of Buccleuch and other breeders, sent north two Black Horses of his own breeding which were stationed alternately, three days a week at the Crown Hotel, Linlithgow, and at quarters in the Edinburgh Grass Market. These horses were made much use of and Black Horse blood as distinct from old type Clydesdale came into general demand.

One of Bakewell's stallions known as Young Sampson, a four-year-old, is described in the *Edinburgh Advertiser* of May, 1774, 'and is allowed to be the best black horse ever shown in Scotland'.

H. CECIL PAWSON, *ROBERT BAKEWELL*, 1957

Colour of the Clydesdale Horse

Colour has always been another question. Deep brown was the preference, especially if dappled, but breeders were wary of chestnut as of doubtful origin and roan was also considered impure, but a stripe of 'ratch' or white on the face was highly sought. Grey was one of the old Clydesdale colours, but very early on Frame of Broomfield showed complete antipathy to it, sacrificing every foal of that description no matter how good. Others followed the example, with the result that whereas greys had been common enough they were soon virtually eliminated. Charles Philips' Merry Tom (532), described as the best looking and worst breeding stallion ever to gain the Glasgow Show prize, won the Highland 1854 and Royal 1855 and he was a grey – as were many top Cumberland stallions of the day. There was a race of grey Glenelgs from Durham which won freely and travelled widely. Robert Wilson had a grey Comet (192), said to have had a lasting influence, but only one pure white (technically grey) foal has been noted, and that was born on Arran in 1923.

ERIC BAIRD, *THE CLYDESDALE HORSE*, 1982

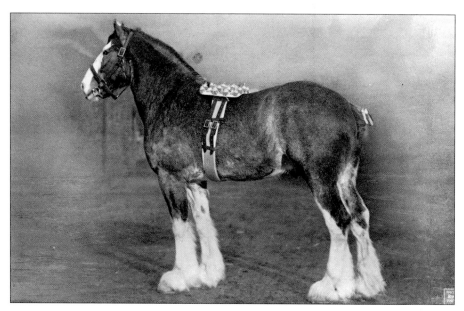

Drumcross Radiant was a son of the famous Apuckwa, and himself won the Cawdor Cup for best Clydesdale stallion in 1915. Shipped to Australia soon afterwards, Radiant left some good foals.

Perfection Gains Sweet Revenge for Ted Cumbor

Yorkshireman Ted Cumbor got sweet revenge at Scotstoun on Wednesday when his big, solid bay stallion, Ayton Perfection, won the Cawdor Cup.

When first shown seven years ago as a yearling, Perfection stood 13th in the line-up, but Ted kept coming back with him.

Two years ago Ted was reserve to Jim Young, Greendykes, Macmerry, East Lothian, when Perfection was beaten by yearling Greendykes Royale.

This year, the placings were reversed. Perfection, on the decision of umpire Hugh Ramsay, Millisle, Garlieston, went ahead of Jim Young's yearling, Greendykes Magnum.

Perfection, now just under a ton in weight, was bred by Ted Cumbor himself. By Ayton Supreme and out of Ayton Jacqueline, he is to stand at Lesmahagow this season.

Perfection was champion at Bingley Hall heavy horse show last year, but Ted had no doubt which he preferred. 'The Cawdor Cup is *the* cup,' he emphasised. 'I'm retiring Perfection now!'

Ironically, Mr Cumbor went home to School Farm, Great Ayton, Middlesbrough, with a new Cawdor Cup donated by Jim Young, who won it outright last year after a remarkable run of wins with good yearlings.

Magnum is by Doura Magnificent out of a Masterstroke mare – Mr Young bought him from Adam Lindsay, Millhouse, Kilmarnock.

The principle female awards went to yearlings. Charles Carrick, Easter Littleward, Kippen, was champion with Littleward Esmeralda, by Doura Masterstroke out of Littleward Mona. Esmeralda was champion at the Winter Fair, Stirling and Milngavie.

Reserve was second-in-class Parcelstown Lucinda, by Doura Magnificent out of Bardrill Linda. James Clark, Osborne Crescent, Thorntonhall, owns her – he had the championship in '60, '61 and '67, and has had the reserve ticket several times.

Three-year-old Monty, bought in the South privately in October by Tom Frew, Hawkhill, Stevenston, Ayrshire, won the gelding championship on his first outing. Mr Frew last took this trophy in 1967.

Donald Henderson, Aynsley, Kintore, Aberdeenshire, was reserve with four-year-old Mac, a son of the Cawdor Cup winner, Ayton Perfection.

Mr Henderson bought Mac at Wigton as a two-year-old and has trained him as leader of his four-horse yoke.

DUNCAN GILLESPIE, *THE SCOTTISH FARMER*, 1986

Clydesdale Realizes Record Export Price

A Clydesdale stallion sired by a Yorkshire-bred horse has been sold for a record price.

Mr Jim Somers's three-year-old Fairways Fascination is going to Japan for £20,000. His new owner is Monsori Hata, Japanese TV presenter and author of many books on horses.

The stallion will be used on Percheron and Ardennes-type mares to impart greater height in the foals. These mares average 16.1 to 16.2 hands, while Fascination is already 18.2 hands and still growing. He was a late foal, being born after the Highland Show in June.

Heavy horses in Japan are used for sledge racing, which involves pulling a sledge weighing 800 kg including the driver in the heats, and 1,000 kilos in the final. The undulating course is half a kilometer long with a compulsory stop.

Fairways Fascination is sired by Ayton Perfection, who was bred in Yorkshire by Mr Ted Cumbor at School Farm, Great Ayton, Stokesley. Perfection won the Cawdor Cup for best Clydesdale stallion in 1986, and was sold at Mr Cumbor's dispersal for 6,000 gns earlier this year.

A Clydesdale stallion.

Mr Somers runs the Fairways heavy horse centre near Perth, Scotland, and in conjunction with Aberdeen University is taking semen from Fairways Fascination before his departure in six weeks' time.

The semen will be frozen and is hoped to be equivalent to ten years of natural service.

YORKSHIRE POST, 25 AUGUST 1990

A Question of Pedigree

The five-year-old Clydesdale stallion 'Muirton Sensation' has had a most outstanding showyard career. He has four times won first place in his class at the Scottish Stallion Show, has once been Reserve Champion, and twice Champion, at this event. He has also been first in his class and Reserve Champion at the Royal Highland Show. As a breed, the Clydesdale claims superiority over all other heavy breeds in its length of stride and straightness of movement. The Clydesdale claims too, the coveted title of 'the breed with the export trade' – indeed, there are Breed Societies in many of the Commonwealth countries where the Clydesdale has been popular for many years.

When choosing livestock, pedigree is a guarantee of pure-bred quality.

FARMER'S WEEKLY, 10 JUNE 1955

'The Clydesdale's Back is to the Wall'

The trend of the Clydesdale trade today puts me in mind of an incident that occurred four years ago when I was travelling on the Canadian Pacific Railway. I was joined by two elderly business gentlemen, and over a good cigar and a drop of the real Scotch, only obtainable abroad nowadays – do you remember that nice mellow stuff that slipped over like honey – we had a grand crack, and my newly-met Canadian friends told me of all the things that needed to be done to put Canada right.

After listening to them for some time, I asked what they thought of the plight of Britain. They replied with no hesitation that they were not afraid for the Old Country, that Britain muddled along until her back was up against the wall, then she really began to fight and soon came out on top.

To my mind, this just about sums up the position of the Clydesdale trade today. We breeders have been muddling along while the decline in the trade has become progressively worse, and it now looks as if we are at the point where the Clydesdale back is pretty close to the wall and the time has come for us to take up a stand and fight for the preservation of all breeds of draught horses, and especially the Clydesdale.

During the war and post-war years every other kind of farm stock was boosted along, and, in my memory, no class of stock has ever had to take the knocks that the draught horse breed of this country has suffered from various causes. One of the first knocks was grass sickness, which first appeared amongst a camp of Army horses at Barry, in Angus, in 1908. During the first few years the spread of this disease was slight, but as the years rolled on it gathered in momentum, and one found it springing up first along the river banks and valleys and then spreading over most of Scotland. Usually fit, young and able horses were the victims of this dire disease, which left in its path many a depleted stable. This affected many men who had taken a pride in keeping a stable of good geldings and who were the very backbone of the trade as they were usually good buyers of young horses at the back-end annual sales.

The continued recurrence of this grass sickness on many farms was the despair of the farmers and provided a favourable opening for the tractor. Up to date science has not yet discovered the cause of or cure for this sickness.

The decline in the breed was gradual until the last six or eight years when it increased at an alarming rate, chiefly due to the unbalanced state of the whole country after upheaval caused by the war years and the boosting of subsidies for all other forms of live stock. One would find that on a farm which had been run on balanced lines for years that the foal's box was needed for the extra Ayrshire heifer, and the following year the odd horse box at the end of the stable was needed for pigs, and finally the stable itself, where many a proud

Roan Clydesdales make striking drum horses.

horse had stood, and where many a whistling, contented ploughman had tied up the tails on a spring morning, was needed for a hen battery. Where can one lay the blame for all this? It is a difficult question.

Unrecognised Skill

At the start of the war the Government gave a lead to mechanization by setting up mechanized units for hire to farmers at a very low rate and at a terrific loss to the country. I feel sure that many a man could have tilled his hand with the horses he owned at that time, but he took advantage of the cheap rates and sat back in the breechin'.

From then on we had a heavy spate of tractor propaganda, with an ever-increasing improvement in all mechanical machinery, while, on the other hand, no effort was made to improve horse-drawn implements and very little was done to advertise the many advantages of the horse, which had served us ably and well down through the years.

By no means the least cause of the decline was the acute shortage of skilled labour, and, for this reason alone, many a farmer has been forced, against his will, to put his horses down the road and sink yet more deeply into mechanization. Looking back over the years to the days when there were plenty of good horsemen to be had, the skill and craftsmanship of these men was never fully appreciated. They started their apprenticeship in many cases long before leaving school by willingly spending all their spare time helping with whatever job was going on on the farm. Usually by the time the lads were fifteen or sixteen they were first-class horsemen fit and able to go away with their pairs to any job, and by the time they were twenty they were highly-skilled men. This was not recognized by the public, nor in many cases by farmers for the simple reason that they were just taken for granted.

HUGH McGREGOR, *THE SCOTTISH FARMER*, 1 JANUARY 1955

Part of a Way of Life

Looking back over some old newspaper cuttings the other day I came across one referring to the number of Clydesdale stallions licensed by the Department of Agriculture for the years 1920–39. The numbers fell progressively from 674 in 1920 to below 400 for the period extending from 1927 to 1933 inclusive, the fall coinciding, and probably in part due, to the bad times through which farming was passing and when the dog and stick went round the fields more often than did the horse and plough.

It would be difficult to over emphasise all that is owed to the heavy horse and to those who breed him or to deny that the elimination of the horse hasn't meant anything more than a changeover from one motive power to another. The heavy horse, and the bond of affection and respect between him and his master, was part of a way of life in the country that has almost disappeared and for which machinery, no matter how efficient and wonderful, has no compensation.

HUGH McGREGOR, *THE SCOTTISH FARMER*, 1 JANUARY 1960

Select Clydesdale Stud Book, 1884

This was an attempt by Lawrence Drew to combine the best in Shire and Clydesdale. It soon foundered following his death.

1   PRINCE OF WALES

Dark brown, foaled 1866. *Bred by* Mr J.N. Fleming, Knockdon, Ayrshire. The *property of* Mr Lawrence Drew, Merryton, Hamilton.
Sire, General.
Dam, Darling.
Paternal grandsire, Sir Walter Scott.
Maternal grandsire, Samson *alias* Logan's Twin.

REMARKS
Gained First Prize at Glasgow as a two year old colt in 1868, and First Prize at the Royal Society's Show, Manchester, 1869. First Prize at the Highland and Agricultural Society's Show at Edinburgh in 1867, and at Kelso in 1872. Winner of the Gold Medal at the Highland Society's Show at Stirling, 1873.

2   DARNLEY

Brown, foaled 1872. *Bred by* the late Sir William Stirling, Maxwell, of Keir, Dunblane. The *property of* Mr David Riddell, Blackhall, Paisley.
Sire, Conqueror.
Dam, Peggy.

REMARKS
Gained Premium at Glasgow Stallion Show in 1876 and 1877, and First Prize and Champion Cup at Highland and Agricultural Society's Show at Edinburgh, 1877, and Champion Cup at Dumfries in 1878.

Prince of Wales, foaled 1866. This Clydesdale stallion was first at the Royal and the Highland in 1869 and first at Kelso in 1872.

A six-year-old Black Shire stallion, bred by Robert Bakewell of Dishley, Leicestershire, 1791. Dishley Grange is in the background. (From the aquatint by Francis Jukes after John Boultbee (1753–1812))

3   **CROMWELL**

Dark brown, foaled April, 1878. *Bred and owned by* Mr Lawrence Drew,
Merryton House Farm, Hamilton.
Sire, Prince of Wales (No. 1).
Dam, Beatrice.
Paternal grandsire, General. Paternal granddam, Darling.
Maternal grandsire, Lincolnshire Lad.

REMARKS
Selected for the Cantyre District, 1883.

4   **BOLD BRITON**

Dark brown, foaled June, 1879. *Bred and owned* by Mr Lawrence Drew,
Merryton Home Farm, Hamilton.
Sire, Prince of Wales (No. 1).
Dam, Justine (No. 139).
Paternal grandsire, General. Paternal granddam, Darling.
Maternal grandsire, Lincolnshire Lad.

REMARKS
Travelled in the Dunfermline District of Fifeshire, 1882. Gained the Premium for
the District of Easter Ross, 1883. Gained Third Prize at the Highland and Agricultural Society's Show Inverness, 1883, and Premium for Cantyre District, 1884.

5   **PREMIER PRINCE**

Light brown, foaled May, 1880. *Bred and owned by* Mr Lawrence Drew,
Merryton Home Farm, Hamilton.
Sire, Prince of Wales (No. 1).
Dam, Flora (No. 128).
Paternal grandsire, General. Paternal granddam, Darling.
Maternal grandsire, Lincolnshire Lad.

REMARKS
Gained Second Prize at Glasgow Agricultural Show, 1881. First Prize at
Hamilton, 1881. Selected to travel in the Kintyre District, 1883. Gained
Premium for Kintyre District, 1884.

DREW'S SELECT CLYDESDALE STUD BOOK, 1884

five

Suffolk

The chesnut breed of East Anglia has its roots deep in the English countryside. It engendered a race of highly skilled horsemen and has inspired clever pens to write of its background and breeding. The breed's society has been as fortunate in its secretaries as have the rival societies, a considerable claim in view of the unstinted devotion exemplified by administrators of all classes of livestock. Few have worked more assiduously for less monetary reward. Foremost among them was Herman Biddell. He was the architect of Volume I of the *Suffolk Horse History and Stud Book*. There is no stud book in Britain, and probably not in the world, to match it. The leather spine on my copy is as smooth as a Suffolk ready for the show ring. Its 721 pages contain some of the finest ever horse illustrations, and a remarkable aspect is the minimal change in type between those animals of over a century ago and now.

Duvall has drawn Mr A. Biddell's Pride 74, standing before a fence with stile, and two mares and two foals in the background. She would have graced the breed shows of the 1990s, as would Mr T. Crisp's Liverpool Captain 422, foaled in 1835. The stud book lithograph was from a drawing by Mr Duvall from Mr Davis of Chelsea's picture, which was also the subject of an engraving in the *Farmer's Magazine* 1841.

Any Suffolk enthusiast would be delighted to use Liverpool Captain today. 'He was said to be a very handsome horse and of quite the Suffolk type', reads the caption. The lure of the breed has been a constant thread in a considerable corner of the English countryside for a century and a half, epitomizing all that is good, and linking human and equine families in strenuous work and spirited competition right up to the present day.

George Ewart Evans – A Tribute to a Welsh Historian of the Suffolk Heavy Horse by a Scot

'The heavy horse has re-established himself in the consciousness of hundreds and thousands of people who had almost forgotten his existence, and there is now no danger at all of his becoming a dying breed.'

Mr A.W. Crisp's Matchet.

George Ewart Evans, who died earlier this year, wrote that sentence in *Horses Power and Magic*, the latest of a series of books in which he chronicled the agricultural past of East Anglia, and by doing so helped to make 'hundreds and thousands of people' more aware of the heavy horse world.

This chronicler of the most English of Englands was himself a Welshman, born in the mining town of Abercynon, in Glamorgan. After service in the RAF he intended to resume as a teacher but said: 'I came out of the Air Force quite deaf, and was advised that deaf teachers were not much in demand'. Instead, it was his wife who was the teacher, in Blaxhall in Suffolk.

There, he found that 'the people were historical documents – books that walked' and he began to amass the material which produced a remarkable series of books.

After reading through them once again, I realize that he never quite believed that the farm horse was gone for good, or that the old horseman was right when he told him 'before long, if you want to see a farm-horse you'll have to visit a zoo' but he was agreeably surprised by the extent of the revival.

The first books set the dividing-line between the new and the old at 1895. Those born before that date belonged to the old way, those born after (and moulded by the First World War) belonged to the modern world. Later he was happy to revise that opinion, finding that oral tradition had persisted much better than he could have hoped.

Evans, a political radical, did not see the old ways through rose-tinted spectacles. 'The set-up on some of the farms during those years, as related by the old horsemen was anything but idyllic; and the description they gave of the rivalry, back-biting and sometimes open malice that existed, even among the men themselves, should be taken into account when there is any impulse to depict the countryside under the old order as a haven of peace and rural contentment.'

He was fair to the landowners. 'Only when they became afraid that there was a direct challenge to their class interests did they act cruelly; in these circumstances even the most humane squire was quite capable of using the steel fist.'

Nor was he blind to the advantages the machine brought to the countryside. Those who have lived through the change will agree that 'It has largely taken the back-breaking and debasing toil out of farming – a tremendous gain in itself' and that it has given the farm-worker the conditions for better living.

Good horsemanship paid. 'There was little sentiment about it; every scrap of knowledge relating to the farm horse was an atom of power which the holder could use to his best advantage to make his job easier, or even to retain his job at the time of the farming depressions.'

The more he learned of the old horsemen, the less he believed in magic. What had seemed to him in the early years to be quite beyond rational explanation turned out as he dug deeper to have a logical and rational cause. 'My experience over many years of trying to find the pattern of those so-called magical practices convinces me that there was in fact nothing magical about it at all.' Some 'magic' he could not explain. How could a horseman stick a fork in a dunghill in such a way that a team of horses straining on the traces attached to it could not move it?

To a Scot who has spent happy times in the company of 'made horsemen' who have the Grip and Word, it was interesting once again to read his detailed account of the links between the old horse culture of North-East Scotland and that of East Anglia. My impression is that the culture was much stronger in Scotland. Evans reckoned that on ninety-nine out of a hundred farms in Suffolk, the 'Horseman's Word', to give a comprehensive name to the whole corpus of practice, was never heard of, or even if dimly known was not known well enough to be practised.

One of the big differences between the two countrysides is the breed of horse. To an eye used to Clydesdales, or even Shires, the low position of the Suffolk's shoulders gives an impression of squatness allied with power.

Even so, the breed has come a long way. Evans more than once quoted Arthur Young's description of the unimproved horse as it was around 1750. 'I remember seeing many of the old breed which were very famous, and in some respects an uglier horse could not be viewed; sorrel-colour, very low in the fore-end, a great ill-shaped head with slouching heavy ears, a great carcase and short legs, but short backed and more of the *punch* than the Leicestershire breeders will allow. These horses could only walk and draw; they could trot no better than a cow. But their drawing power was very considerable . . .' (The Leicestershire breeders were those who were working on the Black Horse, later the Shire.)

Evans wrote with affectionate admiration of the present-day Suffolk, with his beautiful chestnut colour and round lines. 'He is a compact horse, called Punch because like Mr Punch he is short-legged and barrel-bodied, in fact a short fat fellow. His hardy build, his determination, his long working life and his quickness at starting, and his ability to go long hours without feeding, have made him an ideal horse for the plough.'

That a man should build such a monument of oral history though very deaf is a tribute to what in Scotland we would call his 'thrawnness', his stubborn determination. But what shines through is a kind and caring man. He approved of what the old horseman wrote about horse trading: 'Use judgement, justice and mercy, and teach them to fear, love and obey'.

DUNCAN GILLESPIE, *HEAVY HORSE WORLD*, 1988

The Suffolk Punch

Much has been written of the admirable qualities of the Suffolk Punch, a now accepted sobriquet derived from the physical characteristics of the breed. Barrel-chested, deep in the body with short, powerful, stocky, 'clean' legs, the Punch-like appearance of the 'roly-polies' as I have heard them called in Essex, has attracted affection as well as admiration among devotees of the heavies. As a breed its characteristics have been remarkably stable and the tenacity of the distinctive chestnut shades [The shades range from the most popular and characteristic bright chestnut, through golden, red, light mealy, dark, mahogany and near brown-black.] of the old breed, despite the introduction to Suffolk mares of a dark Lincolnshire heavy, is evident. Around 16 hands, they present a good strong head, marked with a white star and blaze, fine shoulders, a compact body and a prominent rounded rump. They move well and surely and, because of their power and stamina, have served for haulage and as artillery horses although their authentic role is on the land. Temperamentally the Suffolk Punches are commonly regarded as willing, docile, without vice, and industrious. They will 'wuk all day' on short commons and pull until they drop or are relieved at 'off-collarin'. No other horse will out-work the Suffok at the tasks for which they have been bred. The intractable clays of East Anglia and Essex have yielded to the endurance and spirit of these indefatigable animals who, in their day, have toiled in the nation's granary to earn their unstinted reputation among those who know their worth.

K.J. NEALE, *THE 'COLONY' SUFFOLKS*, 1975

Suffolk Molly

Master and Molly were not speaking.
To say he had a thing about her
was gross understatement.
'She' spoilt the balance of his Suffolk stable.
'She' had no golden sheen to catch
the glancing sun
but shadow dark, near to blackness
when the rain was on her.
'She' made a proper fool of him at haytime.
He took to rake and an hour later
had done about everything bar that!
Red faced, he cursed her, 'Damned bitch.
She's only got one gear – an' that's reverse!
An' another thing. She's too tired ter stand up!
Why, last spring when filling drill wi' bag muck
fer tater rows – she fell down in't shafts
three times. ASLEEP! Lord help us! . . . '

The Master's constant theme 'She's' fer the
knacker's yard' cut no ice with Waggoner.
'Cept one day, all quiet like, he said,
'Master! Ye mark my words. If Molly
goes, I go . . .'
Ye see, Waggoner saw it different.
E'd shake 'is 'ead and say,
'Black she may be, but 'er eart is gold.
Jes' watch 'er pull a load of beet from out
the plodging mire.
As fer hay-rake job. I reckon some
cruel bastard lit straw beneath her, when
she jibbed when young,
An' lit a fire of fear within her gut
whenever rake tines jangle.
Sleep! Master? I reckon that be Molly's right.
Twenty years she's borne the winter's spite,
an' sweated buckets 'neath the summer sun.
. . . Ye have cure enough in an eye
that's sharp and in the cutting edge of
the tongue's whip.

Suffolks working in the fields.

> But allus let yer 'ands be kind.
> Let 'er be I say. She be a Suffolk proud.
> Old England's fairer for her breed.'
>   DAVID B. NIXON, *PICTURES ON A WALL*, 1983

Suffolk Horsemen

A pair of Suffolks was responsible for ploughing about 50 acres of land during the year; and Suffolk farmers up to the coming of the tractor discussed the size of a farm in relation to the number of plough-teams it supported, in much the same way as the Domesday scribes characterized the farms in their survey of 1086. The phrase a *twelve-horse farm* told a Suffolk farmer or farm-worker the main points he needed to know about a holding: it would be about 250 acres in extent, probably a little more; it would have five regular plough-teams and perhaps a pair of older horses kept for *jobbing*, carting and doing some of the lighter work necessary on the farm.

The East Anglian horseman, who was also the ploughman – tending the horses as well as ploughing with them – took a great pride in his teams and in the standard of the work he did with them in the field. We get the picture of his walking round the parish on a Sunday morning during the ploughing and drilling season, weighing up his own work against that of his neighbours.

George Sadler, the Cambridgeshire farmer, mentioned the care the horsemen took to keep their horses in condition:

'Look at the competition in those days. There'd perhaps be twenty stables of horses in one village. And they'd all be out to see whose horses would come out the best. Look at the pride they'd got in them. If you had horses yourself and somebody said to you:

'"Have you seen old So-and-So's horses? I've never seen horses like them in my life!" As soon as you went home that night you'd think to yourself: "Well, I'm a-going to beat him if I can," and you'd feed up your horses till they glowed.'

So intent was he on feeding his horses well and keeping them in a condition which the rest of the farms could look at with envy that he would try to scrounge extra rations for his horses from wherever he could:

'We used to roll oats for horses' food, my brother and me; and we used to pinch a sack or two of these oats and put it in the chaff. We used to dig a hole right down in the chaff-house and put a sack or two of these extra oats in there. Because we were allowed two hundredweight of oats a horse a week, and a hundredweight of maize when they were working hard. I used to go with my brother when he used to grind the oats and roll them out; and about this time I recollect we had a field of wheat and it looked a bit thin, not too heavy a crop. So we drilled some spring oats in it. Well, after that field was harvested we thrashed that corn out. Blast, it was some good grub. We used to soak it in an old tub. And the horses! well, after they'd been on that for a bit, their coats were just like raven feathers.'

George Sadler also told me how as a young lad working on his father's farm he used to help himself to the shepherd's food to feed to his horses, just to ensure they would look at least as well as anyone else's horses in the parish.

GEORGE EWART EVANS, *THE FARM AND THE VILLAGE*, 1969

Barber Moyse

In November 1862 a party of the oldest and best informed leaders in the neighbourhood agreed to meet at the editor's house for the purpose of recalling facts, histories, and pedigrees which were fast receding into the land of oblivion. To arrest these precious records of history – which had no existence except in the memories of those elderly men – notes were taken, and although

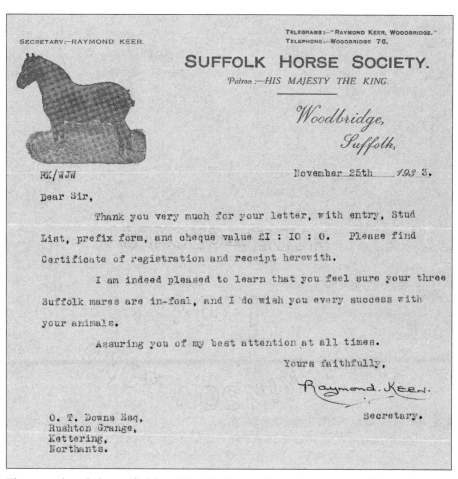

The personal touch that typified the relationship between the society secretary and its members.

no special plan was in prospect for utilising the information, the memoranda were all preserved. Fifteen years afterwards they were turned to account. The torrents of fact which the party poured forth was a history in itself, and to have secured it all, the services of a professional reporter should have been employed. That which I did manage to place on record was ample to show that the materials for a stud book were in existence, if only means were taken to collect them. These meetings were repeated, one was much like another, but fresh histories were forthcoming at every gathering; rich stores of reminiscence to harvest, with the constant apprehension that much must be lost where each had something to tell, all spoke out at once, and one only was present to collect the spoil.

It was at one of the earliest of these meetings that I was introduced to the name of old John Moyse. To those who knew that extraordinary man, the value of the introduction will be readily understood. Born in 1789 at the Queen's Head, at Stradbroke, and apprenticed to a barber at Halesworth, he commenced business at Earl Soham. Here he took to colt-breaking; shifted his tent to Occold, near Eye, became a dealer in horses, and removed to Framlingham. There he failed in the horse business, and once more set up his pole, and after resting on his oars for a time became a recipient of one of the town charities, and eventually ended his days in Sir Robert Hitcham's Alms House.

A lad when the century came in, he lived till close upon ninety years old: having made Suffolk horses the study of his life, and with a memory that retained every particular from his boyhood, his knowledge of the subject was something marvellous. He was, literally speaking, a walking stud book. It was not, however, till a search through the files of the county papers of the last seventy years had tested his accuracy that the full force of his memory became apparent. Born in High Suffolk, at that time the very centre of the district most celebrated for the breed, and travelling through the Eastern part of the county all his life, there was scarcely a horse of note, which had been in existence during the century, that he could not minutely describe. At the time I first became acquainted with him, he knew nearly every travelling horse in East Suffolk, and the ease with which he would glide off into a long line of pedigree and give you a history as he went along was delightful. His manner of telling a tale was quite Yorkshire. 'Yes, sir, they did say he was nice kind o' colt, but had na faet ye know, sir. Oh, yes, a verra pretty horse, but I like 'em with good fa-et. Don't you, sir?' Another was 'a *beautafall* horse, and a verra sho't legged 'un too, sir.' Had the *Stud Book* been started when this old worthy was in his prime, many a blank in its pages would have been filled up, and not a few of the entries where the pedigrees are wanting would have appeared in full with a note or two of description as well. But Moyse was mortal, and Moyse died; and although much of the *Stud Book* came from his recollections, the task of editing its pages would have been all the lighter for his help to complete it.

HERMAN BIDDELL, *THE SUFFOLK STUD BOOK VOL. I,* 1880

'Halloaing Like a Boy'

It was said of a celebrated statesman, that he was born at forty-five, and till death closed his account on the verge of what, in any other man, would have been his eightieth year, never got any older. The late Mr Charles Frost, of Wherstead was some such a character. 'Age? What can age do with a man who gets to the prime of life, and keeps there?' So said some one of him when a long way the wrong side of seventy he was seen tearing over the plough, through the bushes and halloaing on the hounds like a boy. To those who knew Mr Frost but a few years ago, that was what he was like. The 'Evergreen' was his name. But alas, patient, plodding, inevitable time overtook him at last, and a few months ago this fine old Englishman died.

Mr Frost had been at Wherstead a good many years. It is said he began with some very moderate stock. His horses are reported to have been bred from anything but a first rate origin. He told me himelf within a few weeks of his death that he never gave more than five-and-thirty pounds for a cart horse in his life. If, however, a breeder persists in crossing the meanest of mares with the best blood to be had, the result comes right at last. This must have been the plan which was adopted by Mr Frost, for of all the names that occur in this concluding chapter of the *Stud Book*, no one has been so successful as a breeder of Suffolk cart horses as the late Mr Charles Frost, of Wherstead. In the catalogue of his sale the following prices are recorded as having been realised for horses bred by him.

	GUINEAS
Sir Colin 544	250
Royal Prince 190	200
Cup-bearer 2nd 542	330
Statesman 546	400
Cup-bearer 3rd 566	200
Prince Arthur 923	100
Belle of the Ball two-years-old filly 415	230

HERMAN BIDDELL, 1880

A First-class Suffolk

The following points are some of the most essential requisites in a first-class Suffolk:

The recognized colour is chesnut. Bays were very prevalent some years ago, but the presence of that colour can, in nearly every case, be traced to the introduction of extraneous blood. Of the chesnut there are seven shades – the dark, at times approaching a brown-black, mahogany, or liver colour; the dull dark chesnut; the light mealy chesnut; the red; the golden; the lemon; and the bright chesnut. The most popular, the most common, and the most standing colour is the last named. The bright chesnut is a lively shade, with a little gradation of lighter colour at the flanks and at the extremities – but not much. It is, in most cases, attended with a star on the forehead, or thin 'reach,' 'blaze,' or 'shim' down the face. The flaxen mane and tail prevalent 100 years ago, and occasionally found at the present day, are usually seen on the bright chesnut. This shade is also not unfrequently shot with white or silver hairs hereditarily distinctive of certain strains.

The red chesnut is a very popular colour; and a red chesnut is almost sure to be a whole coloured horse. There is no variation of shade in it, not even at the flanks, quarters, or extremities. It is said to come of a taint of bay origin; especially the lighter variety – the cherry red.

The golden is a beautiful colour, not many removes from the bright chesnut, but is not unfrequently faced up with a white heel behind. The lemon is a very light golden shade; known sometimes as the 'yellow' chesnut.

The light mealy chesnut is condemned by all; it is indicative of a weak constitution, soft legs and a slow phlegmatic temperament. Commencing with a dull chesnut body, the flanks and under-line are a mottled ash colour, gradually shading off to a dirty white at the extremities, which are usually covered with soft hair of the same hue.

The dark chesnut is a favourite with some breeders, but is mostly a changing colour, varying with the season of the year, from almost a black to a dark cherry red. It has been prevalent from the commencement of the century to the present time. Smith's horse 1110 of Parham, foaled in 1799, was a dark chesnut; so was Spink's Suffolk Farmer 1127 of about the same date. Toller's Boxer 1199 afterwards Spink's 1124, Hunt's 711, and Creighton's Briton 390 was a dark chesnut, and Catlin's Ripshawe 294, Keer's Young Briton 762, Clarke's Briton 321, and Crisp's Cup-bearer 416 were all very dark. It is said to be a hardy colour, but there can be no doubt that a first-class mare is considerably depreciated in value, if a dark, instead of a bright or golden chesnut. The dull-dark chesnut is only one remove above the light mealy chesnut, and is held in little better repute.

From a careful investigation, I am fully persuaded that wherever the bay crops out there is some infusion of impure blood to account for it. The strains which have a taint of extraneous origin are those in which the bays were most common. It is seldom met with now, and where it does occur is almost invariably to be accounted for by a known stain in the pedigree. A further reference to the origin of the various shades of colour will be found in the history of the breed. Sorrel was the name by which the chesnut was known many years ago. Black, white, grey, or dun is never mentioned in connection with the colour of a Suffolk horse.

So far as a leading feature in his character, colour stands first. Next to it comes that indescribable but equally unmistakeable element in his composition, which is known by the term of 'quality.' The moment a Suffolk is led into the ring side by side with the Shire-bred or Clydesdale, not even colour is so suggestive of the breed as this essential point of 'quality.' There are chesnuts of

Cheryl Clark driving a pair of Suffolks. (Suffolk Horse Society)

all breeds, and although the especial shade of the Clydesdale or Shire-bred is seldom the exact hue of the bright chesnut of the Suffolk, the difference is not at once apparent, but this 'quality' is a thing in itself. A Shire-bred horse with a cross of something else in his pedigree, may be sent into the show-yard without a particle of hair on his legs (we saw this at Lowestoft in 1879), or a Clydesdale may be shown with a coat like West Australian's, but neither of them would give one the idea of the quality of a Suffolk. Nor is it necessary that a horse of a great deal of quality should be totally free from hair on his legs; it has no connection with a light bone – some of the heaviest-boned Suffolks show the most quality.

HERMAN BIDDELL, 1880

The Duke Family

Capon's Duke 261 had another son – a giant. This was Crisp's Red Champion 435, sold as a three-years-old. But he left Crisp's May Duke 426 to perpetuate the strain of these big whole-coloured horses. The Chart gives an account of eleven of the sons of May Duke 426. There are many May Dukes among them,

Mr H. Wolton's Royalty.

Mt T. Crisp's Cup-bearer.

but perhaps the best stallion of the lot was Mr A.W. Crisp's Chillesford Duke 395, dead now, but represented by Mr Hayward's Champion 680, of Martlesham, and one or two more still alive. This completes the list of the generations of Catlin's Duke 296, which are now in the county. There are many individuals among them which we have no space to describe, but which belong to one or other of the branches mentioned. There were, however, an immense number of Duke's stock sold to go abroad. They were as easy to sell as to manage and feed, and the breeders of Suffolk horses are perhaps more indebted to Catlin's Duke 296 than to any other horse of the last fifty years for perpetuating the true character of the Suffolk Punch – that round, thick-set, short-legged type for which the breed has long been celebrated. We have now reached the end of the Groom's Ramper 636 line, and must turn to his half-brother, the other son of Brady's Briton 198, and trace the descendants of 'Plant's dark horse 990 of Bulchamp.'

HERMAN BIDDELL, 1880

Three Belgian Mares Arrive in Cambridgeshire

Three Belgians have been imported into the UK from the USA by Geoffrey and Sue Wollard of Bottisham, Cambridgeshire. Laura, Linda and Bell arrived in March and the following month Bell gave birth to a colt foal, Bill.

The Wollards, fourth-generation arable farmers near Cambridge, had always admired heavy horses but had never acquired any. Trips to America turned their heads in favour of the big Belgians and the sight of these horses at 1992 West Virginia State Fair finally made up their minds.

Investigations about the possibilities of importing a pair of Belgian geldings led to contact with several breeders in the United States and finally to Bill Hostetler in Ohio. In Amish country the Wollards chose WHF Golden Laura, 12 and WHF Golden Linda, 11 – mares which were fit, well-behaved and seemed just right for beginners.

Another visit followed and they decided to purchase a third horse, WHF Corey's Bell, a half sister of the other two, aged six, and in foal to Circle Oak Mister Verdon, a stallion owned by Jacob Kanagy.

The horses were flown to Manchester where they were transported by Brookfield Shires plc to their new home in the Fens. They were pronounced well by their vet and Richard Gowing, the Soham farrier, checked their hooves, being most complimentary about the state of their feet.

Bell's foal, Bill, arrived on 6 April, a big healthy colt, obviously with a celebrity future in front of him.

Mr Wollard, who says his friend Albert Johnson recalls a near-neighbour of theirs who once had Belgians, hopes his four animals may be the start of a British Belgian Horse Corporation.

ANON., HEAVY HORSE WORLD, 1994

Coloured Heavies

'Teams made up of piebalds were not unusual in the stables of a century ago', wrote Sir Walter Gilbey in *Horses – Breeding to Colour*, 1912. He cited Pirate and Outlaw, painted in 1810 by J.C. Zeitter and engraved by J. Egan. They exhibit distinctive colouration, long manes and tails and as much feather as was general in heavies of the period.

In Volume I of the *English Cart-Horse Society Stud Book* (forerunner of the Shire equivalent) a piebald foaled in 1825 is listed. He is No. 770, Everett's Horse, bred and owned by Everett of Broughton, Lincolnshire. In the mid-nineteenth century B.B. Colvin had a breed of piebald Shires on his Hertfordshire farm, which unfortunately died out after his death.

The Old Strawberry, registered as England's Wonder 761, was foaled in Norfolk in 1861, and was used there and in Montgomeryshire, an up-and-coming Shire centre. He left roans of many hues, 'all with or without white legs, and white patches, and even varieties of skewbald' according to Chivers in *The Shire Horse* (J.A. Allen, 1976).

Paul Pollard's 16.1 hands piebald Saxon brings in straw from the field.

The piebald heavy Saxon, 16.1 hands, is used by Paul Pollard for farm and recreation work. Stable companion Gulliver, 16.2 hands, is in the background; both are popular with the public.

Sir Walter Gilbey stated that parti-coloured Shires 'are by no means uncommon in the Fen country.' Nearer our own time, immediate past chairman of the Eastern Counties Heavy Horse Association Mike Flood of Skeyton, Norwich, mentioned William Peeke, who owned twenty big coloured horses for his contracting business which continued until 1976. One job they did was patching roads by the old molten tar and stone method, for which steady and reliable horses were essential.

William Peeke always said his luck would hold as long as he had a coloured horse. In the year he sold his last one, he died aged 82.

Mike Flood has one regret. William Peeke offered him a coloured yearling colt out of a big coloured mare, of the type he bought from the Romany people, for £350. 'I often wish I'd bought that horse' said Mike Flood. 'The public loves to see big, powerful coloured horses.'

Indeed they do. Each year thousands visit heavy horse centres and events, and in so many cases this is their only contact with farm animals. To them, one bay horse looks much like another, but they can identify the patchwork of a piebald or skewbald, point it out to their children, and watch for it coming around next time. The heavy horse world is heavily dependent on the fee-paying public, and ignores this aspect at its peril.

There is an ingrained prejudice and snobbery against coloured horses by

many breeders and judges of most breeds. Yet the Shetland pony and the
Hackney have always accepted parti-coloureds, and are thriving. In the tiny
Falabella, the smaller it is and the more varied the colour, the higher the price.

This consideration must eventually impinge on the heavy horse world. I
cannot imagine that august body, the Shire Horse Society Council, voting to
accept registrations of piebald and skewbald Shires at the moment! Yet within
10 or possibly five years they will surely do so, for otherwise they will lose so
many registrations and accompanying fees to the several coloured horse and
pony societies now increasing their memberships by leaps and bounds.

Paul Pollard, Birchington, Kent, works a pair of piebald Shire types. They do
mainly forestry and farm work, but also haul a large brake with up to twelve
people on board. 'Gulliver and Saxon are big, hairy chaps who go down well
with the public,' said Paul Pollard. 'They put up with anything, take all in their
stride, and are a pleasure to work with. One day we had two dozen Brownies
clambering all over them!' The seven-year-old Gulliver stands 16.2 hh. and
heavy with it, while Saxon at eight years old is 16.1 hh.

To breed a team of piebald or skewbald heavies is quite feasible (piebalds
are black and white, skewbalds white and any other colour except black).
Bone and feather are fashionable amongst gypsies and travelling people,
especially in Ireland. In particular they have some very substantial coloured
stallions. A blood sample sent to an equine blood-typing laboratory would
show if the stallion was homozygous for the colour pattern; if he was, all his
foals out of solid-coloured mares would be expected to be broken coloured.

HM Queen Elizabeth chooses broken-coloureds as drum horses for some of
her regiments. Though this is a strictly limited outlet, the big coloured horse of
equable temperament commands a premium.

Pinto draught horses are being bred at Double Nickel Bar Ranch, New
Mexico, by Lowell and Gayle Clark. 'Pinto' and 'Paint' are New World terms
for parti-coloureds and, just as America sparked off the heavy horse revival of
the 1970s, so a positive breeding programme for coloureds may well spread
throughout North America and shortly across the Atlantic to Britain.

EDWARD HART, *HEAVY HORSE WORLD*, 1994

six

Percheron

The day when the grey or black Percheron was classed as a 'foreigner' has passed, and its devotees form an important part of the brotherhood of the heavy horse. Its popularity might have increased still further had not mechanization swept away the working horse from the most fertile arable areas. The Percheron survived the tractor perhaps rather longer than the feathery-legged breeds, for it is particularly adept at row-crop work where a neat hoof is an advantage in working between young plants. Today its action makes it a force to be reckoned with on the turnout scene.

There is much to be said for the Percheron as a horse for 'newcomers' to the breeding scene. Its breeders have a healthy competitive spirit but less cut and

Vaux Brewery's Percherons are as familiar delivering beer on the streets of Sunderland as in the show ring. Here they are seen on Smith's Lawn, Windsor Great Park, in 1979. (Colin Fry)

thrust – all are made welcome. The breed itself is small in numbers, though expanding, and its temperament is also in its favour. Most Percherons seem to cope with modern traffic, and though there are exceptions that must be watched for, the Percheron is generally docile, kindly, and will do its best to please.

Its breeders have two great advantages. They can draw on fresh blood from both across the Channel and across the Atlantic. French imports tend to be beefy, low slung and powerful. Canadian Percherons are tall and upstanding. Several of the latter grace the contemporary showground scene, especially in harness.

The modern Percheron is black or grey, though other colours have been found in the past. Its clean legs fit it for crossing with lighter breeds to provide show jumpers, eventers and hunters. This aspect of the heavy horse scene is an economic necessity; in all breeds, the best are bred pure for replacements, but a number of mares can usually be spared for other purposes, and these can provide the sales that help keep the others going.

At the breed show, part-bred Percherons give displays in dressage; the breed's adaptability is an asset in these days of ever widening equine disciplines.

The Percheron

In 1916 Sir William Birbeck, Director of Remounts, sent Colonel T.R.F. Bate, Royal Artillery, and Lieutenant-Colonel Sir Merrick Burrell to compare the various breeds of draught horse at the French Government Haras (stud farm). They and the officer there all agreed that they preferred the Percheron to all other types. Sir William concluded that the civilian population should breed and use a hardier, more active and cleaner-legged draught horse than it was doing.

The English Ministry of Agriculture took up this point from Sir William, and arranged with the French Ministry for the export of two pure-bred Percheron stallions and twelve mares. Lord Lonsdale and Mr Henry Overman agreed to purchase them to start the experiment. A further Commission of highly competent horsemen selected and purchased more animals in 1917. In 1920 forty-five Percheron mares and fillies were imported and sold to home breeders. Thus the French breed's importation into Britain was done in no haphazard manner. Those responsible did not seek financial gain, nor to harm the native British breeds. Their sole aim was to introduce a heavy draught breed of great activity; one that could be bred and used profitably during peace time, yet when mated with lighter mares would produce light draught horses suitable for army purposes.

The Minister of Agriculture, Lord Ernle, told a deputation of English horse breeders that the country's need was for a heavy horse that could trot. In a foreword to a book *The Horse and War* by Captain Sydney Galtrey, Field Marshal Lord Haig wrote: 'I hope it will be brought home to the people of the

British Empire the wisdom of breeding animals with the two military virtues of hardiness and activity, and I would add that the best animals for army purposes are also the most valuable for agriculture, commerce and sport'.

The British Percheron Horse Society was formed in 1918. Its aim was to look after the interests, control the breeding of the animals, and form a stud book into which should be entered all those pure-bred animals imported from abroad, and their pure-bred progeny. That first importation in 1916 is so important historically that it is worth recording the details. One of the two stallions was Misanthrope, an iron grey four-year-old who went to Mr Overman's stud, grew to weigh 21 cwt. and became one of the finest specimens of the breed in any country. The other, Nonius, was also a grey, he went to the Earl of Lonsdale's stud at Barley Thorpe, Oakham. Nonius was foaled in 1913 and did well, though never quite attaining Misanthrope's size. Lord Lonsdale's six mares were:

Name	Year of birth	Colour	Weight on arrival (lb)
Nicoline	1913	Grey	2,016
Kalidaca	1910	Grey	1,708
Mesniere	1912	White	2,016
Limoselle	1911	Grey	1,708
Nive	1913	Dark Grey	1,708
Neva	1913	Black	1,568

Mr Overman's consisted of:

Name	Year of birth	Colour	Weight on arrival (lb)
Irene	1910	Grey	1,913
Navrante	1913	Black – star	1,652
Ninette	1913	Grey	1,904
Niobe	1913	Grey – star	1,540
Neva	1913	Grey – star	1,792
Nodale	1913	Grey – narrow blaze	1,792

EDWARD HART, *THE BOOK OF THE HEAVY HORSE*, 1986

Percherons Again in East Anglia

When the British Percheron Society launched out on its own last month, for the first time in seventeen years, many people wondered what sort of a show it would be able to put on. Its contribution to the Heavy Horse Shows at

Peterborough had been fairly modest (25 entries last year, against 118 Shires), so it was an agreeable surprise to see an impressive display at Cottenham, Cambridge, on 25 May.

There were fifty-seven entries in the show classes and it was significant that these included a number recently imported from France. In the pure-bred mares class, seven out of the ten entries were bred in France and it was a French mare, Cabine, owned by Mr T.W.J. Mott, that won first prize.

In recent months, two groups of Society members have visited studs in France and between them have so far imported fourteen mares. This is one indication of the increased interest in the breed and the need to import additional breeding stock. The first Percherons, two stallions and twelve mares, were imported from France to start the British breed in 1916.

The two investigating groups also had a look at stallions. But last month's show made it evident that we still have some good stallions in this country. This year's winner was the oft-time champion stallion, Pinchbeck Union Crest, who looked magnificent. 'He's never been fitter,' said Charles Cook stud groom of Mr G.E. Sneath, biggest and probably best known of the British Percheron breeders.

The ten-year-old stallion stands 18hh 2½ in high and weighs over 22 cwt. He has already been champion of the breed five times.

Last year's champion stallion, Histon Limelight, was pushed back to third place by his own offspring, Willingham Andrew, bred by E. Bailey and Sons, who own both. Winner of the foal class was also sired by Histon Limelight. These were two examples of the promising new entrants to the show.

Impetus will certainly be given to re-establishing the breed by the Stallion Premium Scheme, to which the Horserace Betting Levy Board has donated £500 and the Society itself a further £100. This was divided up equally between those stallions at the show over three years old and considered to be of sufficient merit, on the condition that they are kept available for service.

In addition to the show classes, there were single- and two-horse turnouts which not only presented some beautifully restored vehicles, but underlined some of the qualities which are valued in the breed. The ability to trot was vigorously demonstrated by a sturdy pair pulling a 1904 fire engine, a splendid piece of restoration by Mr E.T. Sampson, whose stallion and mare were also in the show classes. The long and useful life for which the breed is noted was exemplified by veterinarian Carl Boyde's pair of mares, smartly pulling a Yorkshire wagon and aged twenty-four and twenty-five.

The imported entries at the show made it clear that the French like a plumper animal than we find acceptable, and for this reason they do not work their brood mares. British breeders believe that work keeps a horse fitter and some of them like to keep the mares to light work right up to foaling. A significant comment at the show was that one or two of the earlier imports were already looking trimmer.

Part of the reputation of the Percheron is its breeding flexibility, over its history meeting the needs of war-horse, coach-horse (they pulled the old London trams) and work-horse. The French mares will make their useful contribution, now that the demand for the breed is beginning to grow again, but we can assume that the characteristic British version will soon emerge from the new stock.

The Society reports that a number of new studs have started up in various parts of the country, evidence that the Percheron is sharing in the revival of interest in the heavy horse breeds generally.

LEE WEATHERLEY, *THE FIELD*, 20 JUNE 1974

Edward Sneath

No one better fitted the mould of a typical heavy horseman than Mr Edward Sneath. When he died aged eighty-eight, it was tempting to compare him with Biddell, compiler of the first *Suffolk Stud Book*, who also died 'full of years', and in the place where he had spent his entire life.

One of the greatest Percheron stallions of all time, the black Pinchbeck Union Crest was born in 1964 and owned by Edward Sneath. The groom is Charles Cook.

Edward Sneath was well up to the job of owning the biggest horse in Britain, the Percheron stallion Saltmarsh Silver Crest, featured in the Guinness Book of Records. Twice President of the British Percheron Horse Society, this genial Fenman did not seek wide public acclaim, but was content with his family of five sons and two daughters on the 500 acres where he bred stock good enough to take to many Royal Show and breed championships.

His grandfather entered him aged one as a member of the Shire Horse Society. Despite that early association, Edward Sneath changed to Percherons around 1925; they had cleaner legs and fitted the bulb and potato rows better. At one time his father retained the Shires, he himself bred Percherons, while his son had Suffolks. A pity those family discussions were in the pre-tape era!

Two years after starting, Edward Sneath bought a Percheron stallion, and in the next year two fillies. Histon Ringer was acquired from the Chivers stud. In the 1950s, he bought Saltmarsh Silver Crest, whose grandson Pinchbeck Union Crest was still alive aged twenty-six when his master took his last journey to West Pinchbeck churchyard. The family's nine present day Percherons trace back to Union Crest.

EDWARD HART, *HEAVY HORSE WORLD*, 1988

Speed and Bottom of The Percheron Horse

We have said that one of the distinctive qualities of the Percheron horse, and one which has won for him universal esteem, was fast trotting while drawing a heavy load. It would be, however, an error to suppose that this faculty of fast trotting puts him on a level with the blood-horse. The latter draws little, it is true; but he has a long stride, and as regards mere speed, he beats the Percheron out and out. For the presence upon the turf of such horses as 'Décidée' and 'Sarah,' who have trotted against blood-horses of the first order, sometimes honorably beaten and more often victorious – the presence, I say, of such horses is but a happy and rare exception.

The specialty of the Percheron, quick draft, has, then, its limits, and it is these limits that I wish to make known by means of numerous examples collected with care.

What the Percheron has done in the diligences, mail and post-coaches is known to everybody; and it is useless to repeat it. From one relay to another, never dragging less than two, and more often three thousand pounds, in hot weather and cold, and over hilly, difficult roads, he made his three leagues to the hour easily, and sometimes four; but this was the '*ne plus ultra*,' beyond which it was not reasonable to go.

What he does in the omnibuses, the world that visits Paris realizes and admires. And this is one of the three principal attractions of the Percheron horse to the intelligent stranger.

It now only remains for us to follow him upon the turf and sum up the time made in the trots won by him.

The following list shows the result of trotting matches officially reported upon the turf, and two trials to prove bottom, likewise certified with care, and will give an average of what the Percheron is capable of doing either upon rugged, cut up, or hilly tracks, or upon the highways of a densely populated district.

HARNESSED PERCHERONS

⅞ of a mile was trotted to harness in 1855, at Bethune, by 'Grise,' in 4 minutes 2 seconds.

1¼ miles were made at Mortagne, in 1856, by 'Battrape,' in 5 minutes 4 seconds.

2 MILES–8 RESULTS

The best two are those of 'Achille,' at Illiers, in 1865, time, 7 minutes 17 seconds; and of 'Julie,' at Illiers, in 1863, time, 7 minutes 40½ seconds.

The poorest two are those of 'Championnet,' at Illiers, in 1858, time, 7 minutes 53 seconds; and of 'Bichette,' at Illiers, in 1849, time, 8 minutes 13 seconds.

The average of eight trials is about 7 minutes 36 seconds.

2½ MILES–14 RESULTS

The best two are those of 'Vigoreux,' at Illiers, in 1851, time, 8 minutes 30 seconds; and of 'Bibi,' at Mortagne, in 1865, time, 9 minutes 54 seconds.

The poorest two are those of 'Bichette,' at Courtalain, in 1860, time, 11 minutes 30 seconds; and of 'Artagnan,' at Mortagne, in 1850, time, 11 minutes 55 seconds.

2⅗ MILES–LOADED

Two trials were made at Rouen, by 'Décidée':

The first time, in 1864, drawing 386 pounds, 2⅗ miles in 9 minutes 21 seconds; the second time, in 1865, drawing 408 pounds the same distance, 10 minutes 49 seconds.

A gray mare bred by M. Beaulavoris, at Almenesches (Orne), in 1845, belonging to M. Montreuil, horse dealer at Alençon, performed the following match: Harnessed to a traveling tilbury, she started from Bernay at the same time as the mail courier from Rouen to Bordeaux, and arrived before it at Alençon, having made 55⅓ miles over a hilly and difficult road in 4 hours and 24 minutes.

This mare is still living, and now belongs to M. Buisson, hotel keeper at the

A French Percheron import. Hunotte-de-Courtangis was born in 1973, and owned by A.S. Johnson & Sons. (Colin Fry)

sign of the White Horse, at Lées (Orne), where she still draws the omnibus plying between the railroad station and the hotel.

A gray mare seven years old, belonging to M. Consturier, of Fleury-sur-Andelle (Eure), in 1864, harnessed to a tilbury, traveled 58 miles and back on two consecutive days, going at a trot and without being touched with the whip. This was over the road from Lyons-la-Foret from Pont Audemer and back, a difficult and hilly way. The following time was made: The first day the distance was trotted in 4 hours, 1 minute and 35 seconds; the second day, in 4 hours, 1 minute and 30 seconds. The 13¾ last miles were made *in one hour*, although at about the 41st mile the mare was obliged to pass her stable to finish the distance.

W.T. WALTERS, *THE PERCHERON HORSE*, 1886

The Percheron Horse in England

During the latter half of the nineteenth century many thousands of horses showing strong signs of Percheron blood were imported into Great Britain from North America for omnibuses and for other light draught work in the big towns. It was shown in evidence before a Royal Commission on horse breeding, which sat on the completion of the South African War, that ninety per cent of the London bus horses were bought over in America, or at Liverpool on landing from that country. These horses were undoubtedly the produce of Percheron sires mated with the United States farmers' working mares. Many of them were purchased from the omnibus companies to horse the artillery for the South African war, and proved the greatest success.

Horses of the Percheron type also proved wonderfully good tempered, and withstood the nerve wrack and hardships of the long journeys by rail and sea better than others.

The experience gained of them in the Remount Depots in England and France, and in the Armies themselves, proved that the only rival of the Percheron type of horse was the clean-legged draught horse from Ireland and Wales. And these were only obtainable in comparatively very small numbers. There were so very few Suffolk horses in the Army that it was impossible to form any comparison. The few there were did well.

LT.-COL. SIR MERRICK R. BURRELL, BART., GBE, INSPECTOR OF REMOUNTS,
1915–18, *BRITISH PERCHERON HORSE SOCIETY, VOL. I, 1922*

The Percheron Horse in Canada

French horses were brought into Canada with the early French settlers, according to a record made by Dr J.A. Couture, the Secretary of the French Canadian Horse Society, before the House of Commons, on 17 March 1909, in the following statement:

All of these animals were descended from those sent out from France in the early days of the Colony. Louis XIV, who liked to do things in a grand way, had instructed his Minister Colbert, himself very eager to see the Colony flourish, to send here only the best animals of the Kingdom.

Thus, on the 16th day of July, 1665, there were sent to us twenty mares and two stallions from the Royal Stables (unfortunately eight of the mares died during the voyage). Others were sent us in 1667, including a stallion and two mares for the Ursulines. In 1670 eleven mares and a stallion were landed in Quebec; other shipments followed.

These horses, which remained the King's property for three years, were distributed among the gentlemen of the country who had done most to promote colonization and cultivation.

While, no doubt, the Percheron horse, as we know it today, descended from stock similar to that which was brought to Canada in those early days, the environment and requirements of this imported stock, produced in the following years, a different type to that which grew out of the stock in France.

The vastness of the available lands in this country, which has at all times been at the disposal of the settlers, tended to distract them from specialization in any of the agricultural departments until comparatively recent years. Even today in Western Canada both cattle and horses in some cases roam the prairies very much at will, and it is not an uncommon thing to meet with individuals in an almost semi-wild state, which are quite unaccustomed to the approach of man on foot.

The attention of the ranchers and farmers to horse breeding particularly, has been drawn at different times by demands created outside of Canada during the past sixty years, more particularly in war times. At other times horses have been so very cheap that they seemed almost to be rather a liability than an asset. The development of the Western lands supplied the most consistent domestic demand for horses ever experienced in this country, and it was this demand more than any other that caused horse breeders to pay greater attention to their business, and make real efforts to improve their stock. The following figures will give some idea of the progress made by the different draft breeds since 1911:

Importations

	1911	1912	1913	1914	1916	1917	1918	1919	1920
Clydesdale	1367	1207	646	185	74	92	59	42	70
Percheron	540	560	428	153	201	427	878	882	450
Belgian	114	129	87	45	21	70	161	192	193
Shire	85	90	86	7	5	14	25	19	4
Suffolk	58	24	6	7	–	2	–	5	1
	2164	2010	1253	397	301	607	1123	1141	718

Registrations

	1911	1912	1913	1914	1916	1917	1918	1919	1920
Clydesdale	3680	4062	3614	2835	3132	3859	3172	3313	2794
Percheron	763	825	814	534	632	1027	1190	1521	1213
Belgian	123	139	104	142	91	241	375	265	326
Shire	172	161	169	110	93	118	24	101	39
Suffolk	100	51	75	26	28	22	32	16	15

On 31 December 1912, 6,554 Percheron Pedigrees had been recorded by the Association, and on 31 December 1920, this number had been increased by 16,225 or a grand total of 22,779 in all.

Horses in Canada are frequently handled by people of small experience, and it is necessary that something should exercise common sense. If man and horse both fail to do so, disaster follows, and team owners and farmers now realize that usually the Percheron can be trusted to save the situation.

W.H. WILLSON, SECRETARY OF THE CANADIAN PERCHERON HORSE BREEDERS' ASSOCIATION, *BRITISH PERCHERON HORSE SOCIETY, VOL. I, 1922*

A Distinctive Horse

The Percheron is easy to recognize. Its colour is always black or grey, often with an attractive dapple, and it is found in all the shades between jet black and white. Apart from such differences in individuals, there is the fact that foals are usually born very dark and old horses pale out, often becoming completely white. Other colours used to occur but today no colours but black and grey are allowed entry in the stud book.

The legs are short, large-jointed, with good flat bone, and free from any feather (although old Percherons often grow a little long hair around the fetlocks). The breed is noted for good feet, with hard blue horn. It is deep bodied, with a strong, short back, wide chest and muscular shoulders. The stallions have very impressively arched necks.

The head is very attractive with a wide forehead and fine, gentle eyes, deep cheek and relatively short nose.

It has wide ribs and is also wide across the hind-quarters. Consequently, when mares are allowed to get plump, their appearance is positively matronly. This is particularly true of recently imported French mares.

The Percheron is of course a French horse, deriving its name from the district of Le Perche in north-western France. It has been bred in England for some sixty years now and is beginning to show some differences from the Continental version. In recent years, breeders have found it necessary to supplement the much declined British stock with renewed imports from France, so visitors to the annual show at Cottenham have been able to make comparisons, identifying the French ones by their names in the catalogue, names like Tulipe, Gitane, Diamonde and Hunotte-de-Courtangis. Such revealing names were rare after the influx of the early years, although the 1960 stud book contains quite a few, when five French stallions, a colt and five French mares were all entered by Vaux Breweries.

By the middle of the nineteenth century, the Percheron had been developed into a bigger, heavier and much more powerful animal, largely because the development of the railways reduced the requirements for coach horses. This was also encouraged by demands from America, which sprang from the

The Vaux Percherons make regular beer deliveries in Sunderland.

enthusiastic reception of two stallions imported by Dr Marcus Brown of Circleville, Ohio, in 1851. They were both greys, but American tastes soon turned to the black variety which came close to harming the breed. The Americans also wanted a 'ton horse', which further influenced the French breeders. (There is a record in 1885 of a five-year-old stallion weighing 21 cwt. 68 lb, one of whose sons weighed over a ton at the age of two. Much later, there are two records of perhaps the biggest horses that ever lived. One, given in the *Guinness Book of Records*, is of a Percheron called *Dr Le Gear* 21 hands high and just under 27 cwt. He was foaled in 1902 and died in Missouri in 1919. The other was foaled in France in 1920 and went to America to become the property of a Mr C. Van Winkle of New York. This horse was also 21 hands high and just under 27 cwt. It makes one wonder if the second date is a misprint and they are one and the same horse!)

In the decade from 1880, nearly 5,000 stallions went across to America, along with over 2,500 mares. This preponderance of stallions seems odd to us, and quite different from the pattern of our own imports later. As it happened, many of these prize animals were 'lost to the breed', as the stud book puts it, during the American crisis years that began in 1893.

The first volume of *The British Percheron Stud Book* appeared in 1922. It contained 162 entries for stallions and 440 for mares. The following year, there were 250 new entries, which, considering how short a time it was since the breed was introduced, was quite remarkable. Not everyone was in agreement about the right size for the Percheron. The Fen men, wanting them for the cultivation of root crops, liked a big, heavy horse, around 17 hands and weighing a ton or more.

Chivers had one of the largest studs – at one time it numbered over 300. It was founded in 1918 and by 1948 was breeding over 30 foals a year. It had some very notable champions, including *Limon B704*, and more recently the famous *Histon Limelight B1634*.

Another really big stud was that of Fenman farmer, Arthur Rickwood, who farmed around 9,000 acres in Norfolk and the Fens, and at one time had perhaps 400 horses. (He always said: 'In my view, there is a place for both horses and tractors; the ideal is to find the right balance between the two'.)

E. Bailey & Sons demonstrated one of the useful characteristics of the Percheron, their docility. They run a mare and a stallion together as a pair in a

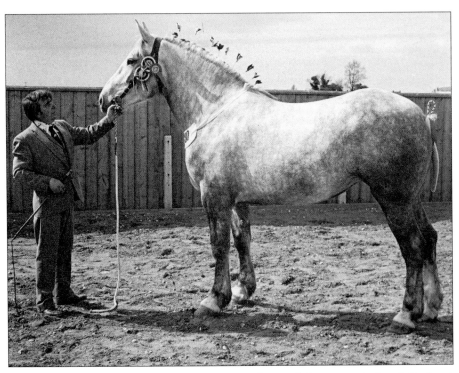

Willingham Varonica, a splendid Percheron mare with great influence on the breed. Bred and owned by E. Bailey & Sons. (Colin Fry)

Percheron geldings, owned by Jim Young of Essex, ploughing on a farm at Cottenham, Cambridge. They are handled by Dennis Hayter of Essex. (Colin and Janet Fry)

A fine pair of American Percherons. (Alex Christian)

A pair of Vaux Percherons in their magnificent new stable block at Sunderland.

turn-out class, *Willingham Ruth* and *Willingham Andrew* (both prizewinners in in-hand classes), beautifully matched and going well together. The French will put the male and female together in this way, too. This means the Percheron is an easy horse to work with, already renowned as easy to train, healthy, a powerful animal and a good mover.

While appreciated as an agricultural horse, he also finds favour with a discerning brewer, Vaux of Sunderland. They have been using horses since the brewery was started in 1837 and at the turn of the century had about 100 horses, mostly Clydesdales and Cleveland Bays. The numbers declined with the advent of mechanised transport, but after the last war it was decided to build up the strength again. This was when the Percheron was first used, obtained from Chivers.

Major A.R.A. Wilson, manager of the Vaux stables, has great enthusiasm for the Percheron. 'In stables or out in the dense town traffic, nothing appears to upset them,' he writes. Their ability to do the work the brewery demands of them and still maintain good condition is due, he believes, to two inherent factors: 'Firstly, a very strong constitution, and secondly their temperament, which denotes almost complete lack of nervous tension'.

LEE WEATHERLEY, *GREAT HORSES OF BRITAIN*, 1978

seven

Stable Lore and the Young Horse

It is easy to clothe the past in a rosy glow of picturesque buildings, willing horses and conscientious men. Yet many of the horse's ills began in the stable, and 'for every good horseman there was one bad one'. Prejudice, ignorance and downright cruelty were too common for comfort. Against this, there were landlords, farmers, grooms and horse doctors working steadily away to improve the horse's lot, as these pages show.

There was something about the work horse stable that made men gravitate towards it. It was warm. The great beasts gave off a certain heat from their vast surface areas, compounded with hot dung and the insulation afforded by hay and straw, sometimes stacked in a loft overhead.

Smells of leather and harness oil mixed with the horses' sweat – but none of these odours offended. The stable's wooden corn bin provided a suitable surface for playing card and dice games, and there was endless discussion about the merits of the horses themselves, both those clomping their giant feet on the floor or thudding them against the stall, or neighbours' horses that could never equal those in the home stable.

The rustle of hay being pulled from racks was a conversation-engendering sound, and the whole stable atmosphere lent itself to good fellowship. Cow sheds, especially modern milking parlours, are comfortless places in comparison. Few spend long with their cattle on a winter's evening, and, as one farmworker pointed out, it was 'better to be kicked to death wi' 'osses than skittered to death wi' an auld coo!'.

Training

The secret of training any horse is to keep it from knowing its own strength; therefore, if it is taught to lead before it is strong enough to break away, and to be tied up before it can break the headcollar by hanging back, it is obvious that less force is required. The horse which finds he can break his halter by hanging

Supper Time, by Mick Cawston. Terriers are favourite companions both in the stable and on the show circuit. (Sally Mitchell Prints)

back is likely to become a troublesome animal to stand tied up, while the one which throws its rider two or three times does not forget that it is possible to get a man off its back; therefore it is better and safer if they never gain such knowledge of their own powers.

The Shire breeding farmer ought to be able to go into his field and put a halter on any animal required, from a foal to an old horse, and he can do this if they have been treated with kindness and handled from their early days.

This is a matter to which many farmers should give more attention than they do, seeing that an ill-trained show animal may lose a prize for no other reason than that its show manners are faulty, whereas those of the nearest rival are perfect.

The writer was taught this while showing at a County Show very early in his career. The animal he was leading was – like himself – rather badly educated, and this was noticed by one of the oldest and best judges of that day, and this is what he whispered in his ear, 'My lad, if you would only spend your time training your horses instead of going to cricket they would do you more credit and win more prizes.' This advice I have never forgotten, and I pass it on for the benefit of those who have yet to learn 'the ropes.'

J.A. FROST, *THE SHIRE HORSE IN PEACE AND WAR*, 1915

Patience, Gentleness, Firmness and Cunning

Until a young horse is trained for work it is not shod. The feet, however, need attention, for the hooves grow and will become too long unless they are *rasped* (filed down). The softer the land upon which the young horse is kept the more frequent must be the rasping. We must be extremely careful over this attention to a young horse's feet. If they are allowed in these early days to become out of shape, the horse when it starts work will develop all kinds of trouble in its feet and legs.

Average good grass on land well supplied with lime and phosphates will keep most young horses growing during their second summer and autumn. The most severe weather usually comes after Christmas, and many young horses receive no artificial feeding until then, 5 or 6 lb of oats and the same quantity of clover hay per day is a usual feed, but this depends upon the condition of the horse, the weather and the quality of the grazing. Unless heavy snow compels a farmer to bring his young horses under cover he will prefer to leave them out with only an open fronted shed for occasional shelter. Such treatment, if not overdone, keeps them tough.

Horses are usually trained for work when two or three years old. They should, however, have been accustomed to the halter and to being led from the time they were quite young foals. This early training makes them much more easily handled later.

'Horse breaking' is an unfortunate term, for nothing about a horse, and least of all its spirit, must be broken. It is a business that needs much patience, gentleness, firmness and cunning. First, the youngster must become accustomed to wearing harness. It must learn that putting its head through a collar is not as bad as it first appears; that the irritation caused by a collar and saddle quickly passes; that it can get used to holding a hard, cold bit in its mouth. The most difficult lesson to learn, however, is that it cannot always have its own way, and this is a lesson that can be best taught to a willing pupil. If the horseman, by his skill and disposition, secures the confidence of a young horse, he will gain a willing servant whose spirit is unbroken.

When the young horse has got used to the feel of the harness it is trained to obey the reins. A horse, to be easily controlled, must have a soft mouth, i.e. it must feel and answer to a light pressure on the reins. Tugging and jerking them, especially when breaking in a youngster, will make a horse hard-mouthed and difficult to control. At this early stage its mouth is tender, and rough handling is not easily forgotten. A young horse is also nervous and quickly tired, and even the best tempered of trainers may find his patience suddenly exhausted, so that each lesson should not last long. An hour at a time is enough.

Next, the horse has to get used to pulling. When first it feels a weight on the collar it will jump forward in an attempt to escape. It has to learn that this is useless and that its master wants it to pull slowly and steadily. This is most generally taught by means of a pair of long traces and a man pulling on each. The pressure on the collar can thus be easily regulated. Later, the youngster can be worked in chains alongside a steady old horse, the trainer driving and his assistant holding a leading rein.

Work in shafts is taught last of all, for this is the most alarming experience of all for a young horse. A heavy implement such as a roller, that cannot easily be run away with, is often used, with a quiet, experienced horse in traces in front. With shaft work a new lesson has to be learnt: that of holding back and backing. Many horses take a long time to become used to the pressure of the breeching on their thighs.

By the age of five a horse should know its work fairly well. It will by then be about full grown, full-mouthed, and the colts will be called *geldings* and the fillies will be mares.

CHARLIE WRIGHT, *FARM HORSES*, 1950

First Steps

The summer had been kind to Moonlight the Shire foal. Throughout the hot days, between play and sleep, he had drawn from the mare's rich sugary fountain, up to five gallons of milk on some days, though always ready to bunt and bully his mother's long-suffering udder with his greedy muzzle for more. For two whole months, excused from all heavy work, the mare had grazed around him in circumferences of care, his silhouette constant in the mirrors of her eyes, while her metronome munch and drag of massive hooves through toppling scented clover were his unfailing lullabies. His body, especially his legs, grew and strengthened with unbelievable rapidity and, now in his fourth month, he was already walking by his mother's side as she worked in the fields, loosely attached to her harness. When the mare worked in trace, he waited, usually with a companion, in the well-fenced paddock near the house, where he learnt to eat hay and crushed oats, and become an accomplished grazer.

As the summer came to an end, and the dark-green mangold leaves met across the rows, and the fields of Little Joss wheat were tinged with nine-carat gold, the milk hairs on the foal's neck and legs loosened and fell away.

On one afternoon, he lay fast asleep, stretched out on the warm earth, motionless from mottled velvet muzzle to black hearth-brush tail, legs rocking-horse wide, blissfully unaware that weaning time was here. A lilt of breeze ruffled his mane, wafted thistledown on to his blaze. He slept on. A speeding dragonfly jerked him half-couchant, ears semaphoring amazement, pool-pupils sun-glazed. The dragonfly returned, cutting through the paddock like a power-saw. Muscles bunched, he soared to his feet with astonishing power and grace, ready to greet his mother with scampering whinnying delight. But she was not there, and did not return that evening or any other, until mother's milk was forgotten and true adulthood had begun.

LLEWELYN JONES, SCHOOLIN'S LOG, 1980

The Dream

Few people have any idea of the extent to which domestic animals respond to personal care, nor what intimate understanding of them is possessed by those whose lives are passed in tending them. To illustrate this I copy out the following note, made last year:

F.S. was anxious about a mare which was going to have a foal, and she dreamt one night that it had two foals, one a fine red fellow with three white legs and a white nose, and the other one a little tiny thing no bigger than a

At Rest. Oil on canvas by Arthur Spooner. (Sally Mitchell Prints)

dog. There came a great black dog and carried off the big fine fellow and left the little one. The next morning she went out and there the two foals were, at the very spot in the Barn Meadow, between the ditch and the apple-tree by the gate, exactly as she had dreamed of them, a big one and a little one. They reared the little one with a bottle, and it lived and was afterwards sold, but the big one fell sick and died after a fortnight. At many other times F. has dreamed of things which have happened, especially with animals she was rearing.

T. HENNELL, *CHANGE IN THE FARM*, 1934

Weaning Foals

Foals should be fed with their mothers on oats and bran at least 14 days before they are deprived of their mother's milk; they should also, for the first winter, have a daily feed of good crushed oats and bran with sound hay, while a good shed should be in the field for protection from stormy and wet weather. This lays the foundation, in bone and substance, for a good horse. A colt neglected the first winter never recovers its proper shape, nor does it attain the size and strength which naturally appertain to its breed.

For sickly, weakly, or unhealthy foals, give daily a teaspoonful of 'ZOMOSAL' in the feed, or in half a pint of milk or ale; or a dose of the 'BLACK DRINK' (from two to six teaspoonfuls in a little warm ale or gruel) should be given for three mornings; and then discontinued three mornings, and so on for six, nine, or twelve doses. A remarkable change will thereby be effected, which will, in arousing and restoring the feeble functions of the body, initiate a state of health which will stand by the animal in its years of labour. The way in which a foal in its first year is treated means hereafter the difference between a good and an indifferent horse.

DAY'S EVERYDAY FARRIERY, 15TH ISSUE, 1885

My Early Home

The first place that I can well remember was a large pleasant meadow with a pond of clear water in it. Some trees overshadowed the pond, and rushes and water-lilies grew at the deep end. Over the hedge on one side we looked into a ploughed field; and on the other, we looked over a gate at our master's house which stood by the roadside. At the top of the meadow was a plantation of fir-trees; and at the bottom, a running brook overhung by a steep bank.

Whilst I was young I lived upon my mother's milk, as I could not eat grass.

112

In the daytime I ran by her side, and at night I lay down close by her. When it was hot, we used to stand by the pond in the shade of the trees; and when it was cold, we had a nice warm shed near the plantation.

As soon as I was old enough to eat grass, my mother used to go out to work in the daytime, and to come back in the evening.

There were six young colts in the meadow besides me. They were older than I was; some were nearly as large as grown-up horses. I used to run with them, and have great fun. We used to gallop all together round and round the field, as hard as we could go. Sometimes we had rather rough play, for they would frequently bite and kick as well as gallop.

One day, when there was a good deal of kicking, my mother whinnied to me to come to her; and then she said: 'I wish you to pay attention to what I am going to say to you. The colts who live here are very good colts, but they are cart-horse colts, and, of course, they have not learned good manners.

'You have been well bred and well born; your father had a great name in these parts, and your grandfather twice won the Cup at the Newmarket races; your grandmother had the sweetest temper of any horse I ever knew, and I think you have never seen me kick or bite.

'I hope you will grow up gentle and good, and never learn bad ways. Do your work with a good will; lift up your feet well when you trot, and never bite or kick even in play.'

I have never forgotten my mother's advice; I knew she was a wise old horse, and our master thought a great deal of her. Her name was Duchess, but he often called her Pet.

Our master was a good, kind man. He gave us good food, good lodging, and kind words; and he spoke as kindly to us as he did to his little children. We were all fond of him, and my mother loved him very much. When she saw him at the gate, she would neigh with joy, and trot up to him. He would pat and stroke her and say, 'Well, old Pet! How is your little Darkie?' I was a dull black, so he called me Darkie.

Then he would give me a piece of bread, which was very good, and sometimes he brought a carrot for my mother. All the horses would come to him, but I think we were his favourites. My mother always took him to the town on a market day in a light gig.

There was a ploughboy, Dick, who sometimes came into our field to pluck blackberries from the hedge. When he had eaten all he wanted, he would have, what he called, fun with the colts, throwing sticks and stones at them to make them gallop. We did not much mind him, for we could gallop off; but sometimes a stone would hit and hurt us.

One day he was at this game, and did not know that the master was in the next field; but he was there, watching what was going on. Over the hedge he

At the close of the day.

jumped in a moment, and catching Dick by the arm, gave him such a box on the ear as made him roar with pain. As soon as we saw the master, we trotted up nearer to see what was going on.

'Bad boy!' he said, 'bad boy! to chase the colts. This is not the first time nor the second, but it shall be the last. There, take your money and go home; I shall not want you on my farm again.' So we never saw Dick again. Old Daniel, the man who looked after the horses, was just as gentle as our master, so we were well off.

ANNA SEWELL, *BLACK BEAUTY*, 1877

Standard Equipment

The equipment and horse power needed to run a fairly substantial farm ninety years ago now seems simplicity itself.

* * * * *

An inventory of Live and Dead Stock, on Mount Farm, which I have this day purchased from the outgoing Tenant, C.A. Jones, and paid for by cheque.
1 April 1907

		£ s. d.	£ s. d.
Horses:	A riding horse, fit for farm work, with saddle and bridle..	32 0 0	
	No. 1 pair, Tom............................. £35 0 0		
	Bob 30 0 0		
	....	65 0 0	
	No. 2 pair, Captain 30 0 0		
	Charlie........................... 22 0 0		
	....	52 0 0	
	No. 3 pair, Stirling (old) 12 0 0		
	Smart............................... 18 0 0		
	....	30 0 0	
	No. 4 pair, Music............................ 21 10 0		
	Colonel 21 0 0		
	....	42 10 0	
	Carry forward		221 10 0

		£ s. d.	£ s. d
	Brought forward......................		221 10 0
Implements:	Harness, four pair cart and plough harness (old and worn)	24 0 0	
	Corn chest...	0 7 0	
	4 ploughs with draught-trees..............................	9 7 0	
	7 carts, old and worn	49 0 0	
	7 framed carts for harvest...................................	28 10 0	
	A gig...	20 0 0	
	Roller	8 10 0	
	Turnip drill (old)	3 0 0	
	2 cultivators	16 0 0	
	5 horse-hoes and drill-harrows...........................	16 10 0	
	4 pair iron harrows and draught-trees.................	12 0 0	
	One pair of seed harrows	1 10 0	
	Iron rake, cart jack, &c.	1 6 0	
	Grass and clover seed sowing machine	2 10 0	
	Potato washers	4 0 0	
	Potato steamer and apparatus	12 0 0	
	38 corn staddles and wooden rails......................	38 0 0	
	Chaff machine and fittings	10 0 0	
	Corn crusher	10 10 0	
	Fanner and 7 sieves	4 15 0	
	2 large pickling tubs	1 0 0	

A young farm worker with his pair around the turn of the century. These horses were probably bred out of farm mares and sired by a pedigree travelling stallion. (John Stone)

120 sacks, at 1s.	6	0	0
Weighing machine and weights............................	4	0	0
Bushel and roller	0	10	0
Sack barrow, shovels, &c.	1	0	0
....	284	5	0

STANDARD CYCLOPEDIA OF MODERN AGRICULTURE, 1910

The Carter and the Stable

Horses have not ceased to be the most valuable servants of many farmers, and so the carter's duties need not be very elaborately particularized here. In the morning he must clean and groom the horses and 'set the stable fair', he must feed and look after them during the day, and late in the evening 'make up for the night'. The cleaner the stable is kept the better, and the fresher the horses will be; but some carters have strange notions about this. There is an old idea to the effect that if the cobwebs, which in some stables hang like dingy stalactites from the rafters, are swept away, the horses will catch cold.

In old stables there is an oak corn-bin or 'ark', with divisions for bran and oats, and a wooden peck measure. It seems difficult now to get the large black oats which were such a valuable part of the horses' food. Carters of the old sort would sooner starve themselves than their teams and by some farmers were given a bad name for pilfering corn to pamper them. For drinking, horses prefer soft water to hard, though now they often get the latter, since most farms have the Company's water 'laid on'. Some country places, however, are still dependent on ponds for their supplies and when these go dry in a hot summer the farmer may have to send his water-cart for miles. A Kentish farmer complained that when the rain came again the horses would not go back to the pond-water and so he had to 'bring them to it gradual', by adding a little muddy water every day to the clean.

The chaff-cutting machine consists generally of a wheel with curved blades fixed to the pokes, which cut the hay as it is automatically fed through a trough; it can be worked by hand, but where any considerable quantity is wanted it is driven by a horse-works or a small engine. This form of chaff-cutter has been known since 1800 or earlier, but a more primitive kind is occasionally seen, though practically never at work. This, in Kent, was called a 'monkey-box'. To use it one had to push the hay along the trough with a short fork held in the left hand, to compress it by treading upon a lever with the left foot, and to cut the chaff by a sawing movement of a knife hinged on another lever. It seems an extraordinarily cumbersome invention, but it was actually quite speedy and efficient in an accustomed hand.

Where the horses' tails are allowed to grow long, they are sometimes plaited with straws and ribbons, and to do this well is no fool's job. Both carters and farmers have often decided views as to how exactly it should be done. The old loose hairs are pulled from time to time and fresh ones take their place. An old farmer near Rhayader made all the rope which was used on his farm with the pullings of the horses' tails, and most extraordinarily tough rope it must have been.

Carters are less employed now as such, for with the increase of motor transport road-waggons are no longer used for long journeys, except in a few flat parts of the country – in Cambridgeshire, Lincolnshire and parts of Kent and Sussex. But wherever horses are kept for ploughing and other farm work, there is a man whose job is to look after them; sometimes, though not so often as formerly, a head carter with a second and third under him. When the waggon was taken on the roads, the carter walked beside on the 'near side' in his smock and with his breeches tied up with whipcord, carrying his whip with its brass-ringed handle and accompanied by a boy or under-carter, for an assistant was necessary to adjust the skidpan or 'drag-shoe' on hills, or perhaps where other traffic was encountered. Often a journey had

The legendary Charlie Butler with 22-year-old Wandle Steve. Charlie became one of the few commoners to have a pub named after him in his lifetime – the Charlie Butler at Mortlake. He was head horsekeeper at Young's for forty-three years. (Young & Co.'s Brewery plc)

to be made to the mill with a load of corn to be ground, perhaps at a distance of five or six miles, and for this the carter had to be up at two in the morning, in order to be back in time for the regular day's work. Five quarters was about the capacity of a Kent or Sussex waggon, and the journey had to be made once a week. Sometimes the distance was more considerable; in parts of Wales lime was carted for fifteen miles, and elsewhere farmers sent to towns over twenty miles distant for 'night-soil' or even farther to attend markets or buy cattle. From the latter it might not be necessary to be back so early, but they might have to start at midnight in order to be there in good time in the morning. In making these expeditions the carter would wake himself at the right hour, and though he had nothing but the stars to tell him the time the position of the Plough would tell him exactly when he must set out.

It was the carter's duty to keep an eye on the waggon and point out necessary repairs before it was too late, and also to see to the state of the shoes and harness. Some farms of middling size kept a forge and a man who could act as farrier, but except on large estates this is very rare now. The occupation of carter was often hereditary, and the horse-bells and brasses were handed down from father to son.

T. HENNELL, 1934

Morning Work

The waggoner's day begins early, for his horses must have a good feed and be given time to digest it before they start their day's work. If they are to start at half past six or seven o'clock the waggoner will be out and about at five or soon after.

From October to April, or thereabouts, the horses on most farms spend the nights in the stable, but during the rest of the year they sleep in the field. In summer, therefore, the waggoner's first job is to bring them in to the stable. He goes to the gate and calls. Usually they come readily enough, and, having supplied a hemp halter on one of them, the waggoner leads the way to the stable, followed by the other of his pair. If there are several horses to bring in, and if some are young or mischievous, help may be needed, and the second waggoner lends a hand.

A horse is sometimes unwilling to be caught, especially when the grass is attractive. A handful of oats, given on the first two or three occasions, may get the horse into the habit of coming readily to hand. For it is largely a matter of habit, and if, for example, a horse has once been driven up into a corner by a crowd, it may be necessary to do so always in future. The man who bustles into a field, and acts hurriedly, or the man who is impatient and is too ready to punish the horse, will be the one who has most trouble in catching it. And serve him right.

CHARLIE WRIGHT, 1950

Good Practice

'A good grooming is worth a feed of corn' is an old adage which serves to show the importance of cleaning working horses. Grooming should not be done while a horse is feeding; when a horse returns to the stable from work in the evening it should be thoroughly groomed after it has been fed. This entails cleaning the coat well with a curry comb to bring the dirt well out from the skin, and then giving a good brushing with a hard brush. Finally the horse may be rubbed down with a cloth. When horses are sweating heavily on reaching the stable, they should not be turned out again until their coats have been dried a little and they have cooled down, otherwise chills may result. In the morning before work, horses are normally brushed but often not combed first, unless their coats are muddy from lying outside.

At certain times of the year the legs of horses carrying a good deal of feather may require washing to remove the mud. This is a laborious process and is not necessary with clean-legged horses. Hairy-legged horses must be kept clean otherwise a trouble known as 'grease' (a bacterial infection of the skin of the legs) may result. Occasionally during the winter, farm horses which are in full work and are housed at night are clipped 'trace high'. This means that their legs and bellies are clipped, rendering them easier to keep clean. It is common practice to tie up the hair on the tails before putting on the harness, to keep the hair from getting muddy. In summer, however, the tails are often left free so that the horse can swish flies off its hindquarters.

Housing. The stable should be spacious, well ventilated, light, well drained and free from draughts. This is especially important where horses lie in the stable at night for part or all of the year. Stable drains should be on the surface, and should empty outside the stable into specially constructed traps, so that smells are reduced to a minimum. The floors should be hard and with a non-slip surface and must be well littered at night. More risk of ill health in horses is incurred in badly constructed stables than in the field, even during cold weather. In the eastern counties of England horses are commonly housed at night during the winter in semi-covered straw yards, the stable being used only for feeding the corn ration, for grooming and for harnessing. Under this system a much less elaborate stable is required, much labour is economized and the horses thrive well, suffering less from cold and chills than if left in the stable overnight.

W. FREAM, *ELEMENTS OF AGRICULTURE*, 1949

Care and Affection

A good waggoner or other stockman has a gift for keeping his animals contented and healthy. This really means that he is fond of them, knows what they want and understands them when they ask for it. This understanding of animals, without need for speech, is largely the result of long hours spent in their company. The way to an animal's heart is not only through its stomach, but a stockman who is thoughtful at feeding time inspires confidence, and without confidence there can be no affection.

Horses in particular like to be given tit-bits, and most waggoners carry 'a little something' in their pockets. The correct way to offer a horse a lump of sugar, a piece of apple or carrot, or any other morsel, is on the flat, open palm of one's hand. An apple or a large carrot should be cut up into slices, in order to avoid all danger of choking.

CHARLIE WRIGHT, 1950

Novembers Husbandrie

When ploughing is ended, and pasture not great,
   then stable thy horses, and tend them with meat:
Let season be drie when ye take them to house,
   for danger of nittes, or for feare of a louse.
THOMAS TUSSER, *FIVE HUNDRED POINTS OF GOOD HUSBANDRY*, (1524?–80)

The Ploughman's Duty

Farm horses should be well attended; the ploughman and boy, if he has one, should be in the stable as early as four o'clock in the morning; the first thing is to clear the racks and manger and begin feeding by giving moderate quantities of chaff sprinkled with oats in a server to every two horses; and this repeated for an hour at least. While the horses are feeding, they are curried and cleaned; and about half past five o'clock they are watered, harnessed, and if done their manger meat, have a little hay put into the rack to eat while the men have breakfast. At six they go afield and continue at work till two o'clock in the afternoon. If at plough, the team performs one acre during the eight hours; but at whatever work they may be employed, the horses, except for some urgent cause, are always shut off at two o'clock. At that hour they are brought into the stable – unharnessed, and have a little hay given in the rack to eat while the men get their dinner. The horses are then fed with chaff and oats as in the morning; and while feeding, are cleaned, watered, and well littered, and left at about half past four o'clock with a little more hay in the rack, till eight, when they are *racked-up* for the night.

Man and horse working together.

After the horses are fed in the afternoon the ploughman must see whether any assistance is wanted from the blacksmith, wheeler, or collar-maker, and get that business done in the evening. Shoeing or plough-share pointing is frequently required: and these things it is the ploughman's duty to attend to.

The harness, both for plough and cart, is usually, and indeed always should be, hung against the wall behind each horse, either upon single or double tucks. So that the collars, bit-halters, hames, and traces may not get intermixed. Plough traces are either chains or hempen; the latter always attached to the hames, the former remain on the whipping-trees, and are hooked to the hames at yoking.

This is the usual stable management pursued among the generality of farmers in the south of England. In Norfolk and other places, the day's work of a team is performed at twice; namely, out at six in the morning, and shut out at eleven to feed and dine; out again at two o'clock, and work till four or five.

MAIN, *YOUNG FARMER'S MANUAL*, 1847

Joe Green

Joe Green went on very well; he learned quickly, and was so attentive and careful that John began to trust him in many things; but, as I have said, he was small for his age, and it was seldom that he was allowed to exercise either Ginger or me. But it so happened one morning that John was out with Justice in the luggage-cart, and the master wanted a note to be taken immediately to a gentleman's house about three miles distant, and sent his orders for Joe to saddle me and take it, adding the caution that he was to ride carefully.

The note was delivered, and we were quietly returning till we came to the brickfield. Here we saw a cart heavily laden with bricks. The wheels had stuck fast in the stiff mud of some deep ruts; and the carter was shouting and flogging the two horses unmercifully. Joe pulled up. It was a sad sight. There were the two horses straining and struggling with all their might to drag the cart out, but they could not move it; the sweat streamed from their legs and flanks, their sides heaved, and every muscle was strained, whilst the man, fiercely pulling at the head of the fore horse, swore and lashed most brutally.

'Hold hard,' said Joe, 'don't go on flogging the horses like that; the wheels are so stuck that they cannot move the cart.' The man took no heed, but went on lashing.

'Stop! pray stop,' said Joe; 'I'll help you to lighten the cart, they can't move it now.'

'Mind your own business, you impudent young rascal, and I'll mind mine.' The man was in a towering passion, and the worse for drink; and so he laid on the whip again. Joe turned my head, and the next moment we were going at a

Three horses in line pulling a snow plough. This was very hard work for horses, who had to breast snow drifts and make a track for themselves as well as hauling the plough.

round gallop towards the house of the master brickmaker. I cannot say if John would have approved of our pace, but Joe and I were both of one mind, and so angry that we could not go slower.

The house stood close by the roadside. Joe knocked at the door and shouted, 'Hulloa! is Mr Clay at home?' The door was opened, and Mr Clay himself came out.

'Hulloa, young man! you seem in a hurry; any orders from the Squire this morning?'

'No, Mr Clay; but there's a fellow in your brickyard flogging two horses to death. I told him to stop and he wouldn't. I said I'd help him to lighten the cart, and he wouldn't; so I have come to tell you. Pray, sir, go.' Joe's voice shook with excitement.

'Thank ye, my lad,' said the man, running in for his hat. Then, pausing for a moment – 'Will you give evidence of what you saw if I should bring the fellow up before a magistrate?' he asked.

'That I will,' said Joe, 'and glad too.'

The man was gone, and we were on our way home at a smart trot.

'Why, what's the matter with you, Joe? You look angry all over,' said John, as the boy flung himself from the saddle.

'I am angry all over, I can tell you,' said the boy, and then in hurried, excited words he told all that had happened. Joe was usually such a quiet, gentle little fellow that it was wonderful to see him so roused.

123

'Right, Joe! you did right, my boy, whether the fellow gets a summons or not. Many folks would have ridden by and said 'twas not their business to interfere. Now, I say, that with cruelty and oppression it is everybody's business to interfere when they see it; you did right, my boy.'

Joe was quite calm by this time, and proud that John approved of him. He cleaned out my feet, and rubbed me down with a firmer hand than usual.

They were just going home to dinner when the footman came down to the stable to say that Joe was wanted directly in master's private room; there was a man brought up for ill-using horses, and Joe's evidence was wanted. The boy flushed up to his forehead, and his eyes sparkled. 'They shall have it,' said he.

'Put yourself a bit straight,' said John. Joe gave a pull at his necktie and a twitch at his jacket and was off in a moment. Our master being one of the county magistrates, cases were often brought to him to settle, or say what should be done.

In the stable we heard no more for some time, as it was the men's dinner-hour. But when Joe came next into the stable I saw he was in high spirits; he gave me a good-natured slap and said, 'We won't see such things done, will we, old fellow?' We heard afterwards that he had given his evidence so clearly, and the horses were in such an exhausted state, bearing marks of such brutal usage, that the carter was committed to take his trial, and might possibly be sentenced to two or three months in prison.

It was wonderful what a change had come over Joe. John laughed, and said he had grown an inch taller in that week; and I believe he had. He was just as kind and gentle as before, but there was more purpose and determination in all that he did – as if he had jumped at once from a boy into a man.

ANNA SEWELL, 1877

Deserted Stable

I sat on the bin that was bent,
buckled and polished by many corduroys,
watching the shafted sun, turn the moss
on the beams to emerald shining.
Whilst a robin sang quiet to himself
the song of Autumn, in the stable
I knew as a boy, now emptied
of scent and sound of horses stamping.
I sat and heard again the voice
of the Carter, putting me right!

'Ye'd no cause ter go an' break
that whipple-tree, in Holly Bush this morning.
Ye turned too sharp ye see. Goin' silly
fast I'll warrant. Allus make a wide
headland, an' give yersel' room ter
turn round. Else yer allus a'tramplin'
on yer work.' Carter paused for breath.
My black hands reached for the Bluebell.
'Better do the brass hames next,' said Carter.
'And another thing. You'll be drilling
Barn Ground in the morning. Take the Suffolks,
Molly an' Captain'll step away lively.'
His sharp eye saw my apprehension.
'Ye'll be alright. Jes' keep yer nose
off yer marker wheel. You an' yer
zig-zag, zig-zag. Yer damned nigh
crippled all the hares in Creation.
'Kip a long line, an' yer head up.
'An' allus, allus, look ter the end of the field.
'Ye'll see yer mark clear shining.
'Aye, even if ground be dry
'yer line will be as straight as if
by ruler drawn . . . '
The bin I sat upon was long ago
emptied.
Only Molly's collar hung dusty,
festooned with cobwebs and
mouse inhabited.

DAVID B. NIXON, *PICTURES ON A WALL*, 1983

eight

Work

Autumn to the heavy horseman means two things – foal sales and ploughing matches. The former are staged in September and early October, but the competitive ploughman comes into his own when the days shorten, mists rise, and falling leaves accompany the sound of the coulter tearing the earth, the creak of chains and the low-spoken commands.

The first ploughing matches followed the invention and subsequent widespread use of Small's plough in the late eighteenth century. It was drawn by two horses. Until then, ploughs had been cumbersome things, hauled by large teams of oxen or horses, and requiring a boy to guide the team for the steering ploughman.

When horsemen met in company, it was natural for them to decorate their horses so that they looked smarter than those of their fellow competitors, and the use of horse brasses and decorations really took off. Many a retired ploughman kept all his brasses till the day he died. Each recalled a day when he had ploughed under a serene autumn sun behind Bonnie and Smiler, or in a storm-lashed competition with Royal and Duke striding out, heads turned against the weather.

Fortunately, sufficient horsemen survived mechanization to pass on the skills learnt in daily contact with the soil. I have seen horsemen handle the single furrow plough, and set its point into the ground to start a new furrow, as easily and as accurately as others use a pen. The plough came alive in their hands, but the life came from the straining Shires, Clydesdales or Suffolks. It passed through sweaty collars and taut traces into the implement that has been proved one of the most useful of all mankind's inventions – the plough.

The hugh scope of literal horse power tends to be forgotten by those who think of a Shire merely as something to pull a plough or cart. A great many devices were evolved during the first horse age that harnessed animal power, transferring it through a series of cog wheels into a means of threshing or grinding corn, chopping turnips or breaking solid slabs of cotton cake.

In the cities, horses performed a multitude of jobs. Gordon's *Horse World of London*, quoted in this anthology, describes in detail the type of horse used for coal hauling, omnibuses, fire-engines, funerals and many other purposes.

The town horse was bred and reared on the land. 'Broken to all gears' as a

126

Charlie Ruocco, Whitbread's foreman horsekeeper, at the company's Chiswell Street Brewery. (Nicholas Redman, Archivist, Whitbread plc)

Horse-drawn deliveries to a Thames Valley pub in the 1950s. (Nicholas Redman, Archivist, Whitbread plc)

five-year-old, he was at peak value. He would go for heavy haulage and, as he aged, often be sold down the line for lighter and less demanding tasks.

This downwards progression was occasionally halted if the horse was sold to a bathing-machine proprietor. In Victorian times these machines lined the water's edge to shield the modest bather from prying eyes, and as the tide turned they were hauled away by horses from the advancing waters. Although each horse had to deal with several machines, it was a life of comparative ease, which, combined with salt water on the legs, rejuvenated many an old stalwart.

On docks and railway sidings, big, powerful horses were needed. In fact the coming of the railways did not diminish the need for horses; more than ever were needed to ply between station and town depot or village store. These horses became surrounded by a cult of their own, engendering a stable lore at least equal to the lore of the countryside.

Alongside Blossom and Daisy

During the winter I often spent a Saturday afternoon walking alongside Bob when he was at work ploughing. Occasionally he allowed me to hold the handles and plough a few yards. Blossom, the tallest mare, walked down the furrow and Daisy walked on the unploughed land.

Bob rarely pulled at the strings attached to the horses' bits in order to direct them. They turned anti-clockwise when he spoke the words 'gee back' and clockwise when they heard the words 'warv up'. Bob often said: 'Ah cud drive Daisy doon a moos ole by just talkin tiv her'. This was the reason that Daisy was the 'fost oss' (first horse) when the mares were yoked to a cart tandem fashion.

When I was capable of using a muck-fork Bob allowed me to help in the stable. He taught me the horse code practised by all farm wagoners. This included entering a stall on the near side of a horse when feeding, grooming, or harnessing it. It was also wise to cultivate the habit of speaking to it first, as a startled horse might react dangerously.

When grooming a horse it was advisable to stand as near as possible to its hind-quarters. If it did kick, contact was then made with its hock instead of its shoe and any injury received would be slight. When I was brushing a horse's hind leg I used to hold its tail with my free hand or put pressure on its hock. I also kept my eye on older horses, as some of them did not appreciate being groomed. A nip on the backside from a horse was not a pleasant experience.

Another code of practice was adopted when an old horse with a raw young-un coupled to it was being yoked to a plough. Strings were attached to the bit rings of both horses. If the young horse became restless the string was handy to hold it in check. The old horse was not coupled to the other until traces had been hung on to swingle-trees. At the end of the day this procedure was practised in reverse. The young-un was the first to be 'loosed out'.

When yoking a pair of horses to a pole wagon it was important to ensure that the traces were the correct length. When the horses moved forward the chains fixed to the end of the pole should be in line with the hooks on their hames to which each chain was attached.

Another important consideration was that cart shafts should be raised to ensure that the horse's shoulder chains were in line with the hooks on its hames. If the shafts were raised too high, unnecessary pressure was put on a horse's back. The reverse had the opposite effect, and the shafts were continually jogged up and down.

In later years I realized how necessary it was to follow one particular procedure. Before turning a horse loose in a pasture it is advisable to stand directly in front of its head, slip its halter off, and then stand back a yard or so.

One day a visitor was standing by a horse's near-side shoulder at the farm where I was employed, and when the horse became aware of its freedom it turned quickly and lashed out with its hind legs. One of its shoes hit the man's temple and he was killed instantly. This tragedy was caused by a combination of inexperience and the horse's high spirits.

HERBERT DAY, *MY LIFE WITH HORSES*, 1983

A Day in the Hay

It is four o'clock on a late June morning. The birds are just beginning to tune up, and a slight mist is over everything as I go down the dew-covered pasture to find and catch the black mare. She is inclined to be skittish at first, but soon finds the handful of maize irresistible and comes to my hand without further capers. We go to the stable to harness up, and then down to the meadow to finish a 'set' (a section of meadow still to be cut). The mowing machine has been left in the meadow. The mare is backed into the shafts, and soon she is ready for work. The pile of grass which had been put over the cutter-bar of the machine is cleared away, and a newly sharpened knife is pushed into it, and the connecting rod slipped home. Then I get on to the seat and, when the machine is in position for the cutting of the first swathe, the cutter-bar is dropped and with a 'suss-a-russ' the grass falls to the flashing knife and is turned by the arm of the grass-board into even swathes. Down they go, grasses, daisies, sorrels, and a few thistles (curse them! for they prick when loading hay with bare arms). The mare is inclined to take things with a rush at first, but soon settles down to a steady pace, and sweat begins to show at the edge of her collar and saddle.

By six o'clock the sun is beginning to dispel the mists and up at the farm the cows are just going into the shippons for the morning's milking. Round and round the set goes the mowing machine. The grass which was first cut is losing its fresh green and is already taking on a blue tinge. Gradually the set diminishes in area, and eventually one end of it becomes a point, as the set was not a perfect rectangle in the first place. Now it is quickly reduced in size, and by ten o'clock I am cutting the last thin line of standing grass. I finish none too soon, for the sun is already gaining in power, and the flies are beginning to torment the mare, causing her to kick at her own belly and constantly to toss her head. I unhitch, and we make our way to the stable, I carrying an armful of newly cut grass for her. The grass is put in the cratch, harness is taken off, and the mare receives a quick rub-down. She whinnies for a drink, but is sweating too much for that, and will have to wait until she has cooled down.

By mid-day the hay which had been cut yesterday is almost ready for carting, for the weather has been good and grass is soon made into hay. It is turned with hand-rakes to expose all the green grass still unmade. About two o'clock in the afternoon, father decides it is ready for carting, and once more the horse is harnessed up, this time to the cart. Over the sun-baked pastures we bump,

Working in the corn field with the Albion Binder.

and into the hayfield where the hay has by now been put into wind-rows – that is, long lines of piled-up hay which stretch from one end of the field to the other. Slowly and methodically the cart is loaded. First, the body of the cart is filled level with the racks (or 'thrippers' as they are called in Cheshire). Then begins the real craft of loading. A large armful is placed on the left corner of the rear rack, another armful on the right corner, and then a good one between them to act as a binder; then another series of three immediately behind them. I now move to the front racks which project forward well over the horse's back, and the procedure is repeated – two courses of three armsful each across the cart. This leaves a hollow in the middle of the cart which is filled with several courses, these serving to bind the back and the front courses. Then I start at the rear left corner once more, and repeat the whole performance again and again until the load is made. Before we take the load out of the field, all the loose hay is removed from its sides with a rake; then, as the cart has to pass over rough, uneven ground, ropes are used to make the load more secure. The load is brought to the side of the farm building, and is halted directly below an opening in the wall – a pitch-hole as we call it. The binding ropes are untied and I climb on to the load. Father and a helper go up into the loft, and then comes the order, 'Let's 'ave it.'

Through the pitch-hole goes the hay; pitching is easy at first for the top of the load is on a level with the opening in the wall, but as the height of the load is reduced, pitching becomes increasingly arduous; the forkful of hay has to be lifted higher and higher, and a good forkful is surprisingly heavy. By this time I am dripping with sweat, and the loose hay seeds fall with the pollen and dust, and lodge inside my shirt. With a last heave the cart is emptied and I yell out, 'You've got it'; and down from the loft come father and his helper, all dusty and grimy. Throats are parched and a drink of any kind is welcomed.

By now a motley collection of village children is in the yard, and all clamour for a ride in the empty cart, so, to their screaming delight, they are swung over the racks into the body of the cart; the more bumps the cart goes over, the better they like it. And so to the meadow for another load. Carting goes on till the falling dew causes the dry hay to 'ungive' as the farmer describes it, that is, the hay loses its brittle dryness and becomes soft.

We unharness, turn the mare into the pasture, and I make a bee-line for the wash-house to get rid of the grime and hay seeds, while father and the men, who have come during the evening to give a hand, hang about and drink beer.

From the uncut grass in the meadow comes the crek! crek! of a corncrake, the sun, sinking redly beyond the distant trees, foretells another fine day.

C.F. TUNNICLIFFE, *MY COUNTRY BOOK*, 1942

The Horses on the Towpath

We were a little backward in developing canals as means of communications. The first real canal – an artificial waterway with locks – was not completed until 1761, while the famous 150 mile long Canal du Midi in France was completed eighty years earlier. However, the Duke of Bridgewater's canal, which carried coal from Worsley to Manchester, set such a good example that the period of activity that followed is usually described as one of canal mania. It extended from the Bridgewater opening to about 1830 and at the end of that time we had some 4,000 miles of canals and navigable waterways.

A long-standing problem on narrow waterways had been moving vessels when neither wind nor current would oblige. The earliest power sources were men, and the hauliers, a notoriously rough lot who roamed the countryside in gangs looking for work, survived until quite late in canal history. Horses were used quite early but in a very limited way because of the lack of towpaths. (The hauliers would climb, or often just break through, boundary hedges and fences.)

Gradually the construction of towpaths caught up and in time horses became the commonest means of 'tracking' boats, along with occasional mules and even donkeys. The tough life of the canals often meant hardship and ill-treatment for the horses until the RSPCA came into being in 1824.

The horses greatly influenced the background against which canal life was set. The inns that had appeared at junctions and canal heads had to provide stabling; the towpaths emphasized the canals' intrusion into town and country scenes. New bridges were built, some of them with special features. For topographical or ownership reasons, the towpaths often had to change to the other side of the canal. Where there was no bridge, the horse had to be ferried across, often in the boat he was pulling. When bridges were built, there was the nuisance of unhitching the horse each time. In some places the bridges were big enough to allow the towpath to run underneath. When the bridge coincided, as it often did, with a changeover of the towpath, 'turnover bridges' were sometimes built. These had round-topped parapets and allowed the horse to cross over without being unhitched. (Not so easy if you think about it. The trick was that the horse went under the bridge first before coming round and crossing it.)

The narrow boats were mostly about 70 ft long and around 7 to 8 ft wide (not to be confused with barges, which are about the same length or longer and twice as wide; many waterways could not accept them). When narrow boats passed each other in opposite directions, one allowed the towline to drop so that the boat, and the horse, could pass over it. Overtaking was not allowed, although battles occurred in attempts to get to the lock first sometimes.

Canals were expensive to build and had to follow the contours of the country as far as possible. Consequently, the canal heads and junctions were usually the focus of 'canal feeders', rough roads that brought coal or other loads down to the boats. These were often 'tramroads' which had wooden rails faced with strips of iron to carry wagons. The rails were flanged, not the wagon wheels. These were routed if possible down a steady incline to the canal head and a pleasant sight must have been a train of wagons, braked by a young lad in the front one, rolling down to the canal head with the horse riding in the last one. After the wagons were emptied, the horse would haul them back up to the top of the tramroad.

The canal companies owned a great many horses themselves, and there were also independent suppliers (known in Yorkshire as 'horse marines'). Stabling was usually provided at wharves by the canal owners, while the carriers provided it at depots. Later, when the railway companies made use of the one-time rival system, they too owned large numbers of canal horses as well as those used for deliveries and shunting.

The great ambition of the canal man was to become a Number One, a man who owned his own boat and horse. Probably this was better for the horse, too, because the sensible boat man looked after his own means of livelihood. It was a recognized thing that the horse came first, even for food if money was short.

Most of the work of the canal horses was at a fairly steady plod, around 2 to 3 miles per hour. A sensible, trained horse would keep just the right strain on the towline and it was no great sweat to keep the loaded boat moving. (The rule was one horse one loaded boat, or two empties.) The only 'uphill' work was getting a loaded boat moving out of the lock. The towpath was often given ridges to help the horse find purchase, but in some places the initial effort was facilitated by a simple device. The towline was passed through a pulley on the mast of the boat and then round a stud set in the side of the lock. This pulley system gave the horse the extra power needed and the towline slipped off the stud as the boat drew level, returning to a straight pull.

A very different pace was set by the so-called express boats which carried passengers and often rivalled the stagecoaches for speed as well as offering advantages of comfort. The first of these, also started by the enterprising Duke of Bridgewater, was not all that fast, three horses managing something like 4 to 5 miles per hour. However, about 1830 a fast service came into being in Scotland that averaged 8 miles per hour and was said to be capable of 12. The teams of trotting horses were changed every 4 miles. These boats were of a special construction, taking advantage of a narrow waterway effect called the primary wave, or the wash would have damaged the canal walls.

To find out more about the last days of the commercial canal boats, I talked to one of the few survivors, 'Caggy' Stevens. He is a Number One, with his own horse, a motor boat and fourteen butties (unpowered boats). He still carries loads – mostly industrial rubbish – on the Birmingham and Fazeley canal.

I asked him what sort of traffic the canals used to bear.

'I remember once, very clearly, in 1933 when I was fifteen' he said 'I counted the boats we met on the 11 mile trip to Walsall Stop, which took my dad and me three hours. There were 164 of 'em, all horse-drawn except one.'

Around that time there was an Oldbury firm of carriers run by Thomas Clayton which had over seventy horses. By 1964 they had only one left which they offered to Caggy, but he couldn't use another one at the time. He has only one horse now, where he used to have five. Canal horses are not usually big, but a favourite of his was Mac, all of 17 hh, who could just about get under the bridges, using his ears like cat's whiskers to judge if he could make it. He used to be a town horse but didn't like traffic. Caggy had him for 'nine years, five months, three days', which is a clue to how much he missed him when he died at the age of sixteen.

Caggy also told me about the ice-boats which were used to break the ice on the canals in winter. In the bad winter of 1947, he remembered seeing twenty horses in groups of five pulling the ice-boat along while a dozen or more men stood in it rocking it to help break the ice. The ice-boats were made of iron and had a rail or rope down the middle for the 'rockers' to hang on to.

There is considerable interest in reviving the use of the waterways and in fact there is quite a lot of holiday traffic on them already – powered boats, of course. However, there are still some horses about. *The Chester Packet*, for example, is a restored 1935 horse-drawn narrow boat which carries various loads in winter and fifty-four passengers in the summer, with many comforts including a bar, between Chester and Backford or Christleton. A similar service is provided at Berkhampstead by a horse-drawn barge, *The Ben Kilbrech*, which can carry up to eighty people.

Whether horses will come back to the canals is conjectural, but there is one thing in their favour. On the narrow waterways, even powered boats have to keep their speed down to avoid the wash eroding the canal walls. The acceptable speed of four miles per hour is little more than the pace of the horse.

LEE WEATHERLEY, *HEAVY HORSE & DRIVING*, 1977

A Wagoner's Life

Hiring took place at Scarborough on the Thursday, which was Market Day. There was a poor demand for men over twenty-one, as we were the highest paid.

Fortunately, I met Bill Grice, a chap I had known when I lived at Abbey Farm. At present, he was the foreman at Wold Farm, West Heslerton, and when he offered me the job of wagoner I accepted.

Shires Jake and Royal being used for a memorable occasion.

The village of West Heslerton nestles at the foot of a long, steep hill, and on the summit of the hill is Wold Farm. Heslerton Station is a good mile from the village on the road to Yedingham, and since coal, cattle cakes and fertilizers had to be transported from the station to the farm, the hill was a real 'bug bear'.

When I arrived at the station after Martinmas Week the road was icebound. I carried a hold-all, which contained spare clothes, and the walk to the farm was one of the toughest I had experienced.

·Nevertheless, I looked upon the Wolds as 'God's own Country', and I had many happy times there. Despite the hard work in hand, it was pleasurable to view on a hillside opposite other men and horses engaged in similar operations to our own.

From December until the harvest the scenery was continually changing. In January the ploughed furrows changed the colour of clover fields from green to brown. The same effect was created when turnips were cleared from a field and the land ploughed.

Before the end of April, the Spring corn changed the colour of these fields to green again, and brown fallows which had been sown with seed would eventually be covered with green turnip leaves.

When ploughing a hillside field on this farm in the early morning of a Summer's day, I have looked across towards the moors, and then gazed down upon a misty, dew-drenched valley. When the sun appeared, the mist rolled away to reveal a bird's-eye view of the countryside in all its natural beauty.

HERBERT DAY, 1983

Single-line Method

First of all what is a single-line? It is not just a piece of rope from the horse's head to a man's hand, it starts at the bit in the horse's mouth, with a small chain coming under the lower jaw to the other end of the bit, the chain was then fastened to a leather strap about 3 ft long; fastened to this was about 60 ft of cord about as thick as a pencil, then the last piece was about 2½ ft of thicker rope with a loop at one end for the man's hand. To train a horse for this method, was when it was pulling a cart; we would walk alongside of the horse and use the first two parts of the line; if we wanted the horse to go to the right, we would jerk the line and say gee-ho; if we wanted it to come to the left, we would pull the line and say walk-up. The horse would soon get used to the way it had to go; it was not the line so much as the master's voice.

All of the horses in the stable we would train to drive with a single-line in this way. But when it came to team work, we use the boss of the stable as a line-horse, and he or she would soon let the other horses know whch way to turn; but it was the way you yoked them together that enabled you to control all three horses just with one line on the centre horse; the two outside horses would have their heads tied to the collar of the line-horse at the chest thong; then from each of these horses' bearing-rein, you would have a piece of rope known as a false-line, tied back to the line-horse's swel-tree; this would stop them from over heading the line-horse. My Dad always would say that this was a man's way to drive a team, any old boy could with two lines. Oh for a three horse team, a plough, a dog, a lump of bread and cheese and onion, not forgetting a bottle of cold tea, no milk or sugar.

C. KING, *HEAVY HORSE WORLD*, 1992

Indispensable

A Clydesdale from the champion British National Ploughing team has proved indispensable during recent wet weather. Prince, a thirteen-year-old brown/roan gelding, has been hauling a heavy crop of swedes at Whamtown, Blackford, in Cumbria.

His driver is Jim Elliott, who has won several ploughing championships with Prince.

'We get on grand,' said Jim. 'We use an iron-tyred cart, with half a ton of swedes at a time. The gateways are very bad indeed, but Prince has supplied our cattle ever since November.'

The Elliotts farm fertile soil so level that drainage is difficult. Most farmers in the neighbourhood have given up swedes because it is impossible to use tractors in a wet autumn.

Prince, who stands 17 hands 1 in, is partnered in ploughing matches by another Clydesdale gelding, Duke.

HORSE AND HOUND, 28 JANUARY 1983

Colour in the Town Horse

'There can be no objection to good hard blacks' wrote Thomas Dykes, secretary of the Clydesdale Horse Society. He was speaking of colour in city horses of the 1890s and, had he lived 80 years later, would have been amazed at the fashion of black with four white legs that dominated the Shire world of the early 1970s. His choice was dark brown with black points, with bays of light or dark shades equally suitable. 'Greys when fully ripe, seem to be higher at the withers than others, while still retaining their gay carriage' was a keen Dykes observation, and he commented that red roans are generally noted for their great weight.

As an aside, one of the most useful and compact farm horses I have seen in recent years was a roan belonging to Mr Ted Dunning of Grange Farm, Whixley, York. The colour is now a Clydesdale one, but that mare would be an asset to any working stable.

'Blue roans are rarely handsome or captivating, but on the average they have more bone than the others, and are great favourites with some London horse owners on account of their hardy constitutions and tractable dispositions' wrote Dykes. 'For the hard wharfinger work off the Thames on the Middlesex side, where all is sheer hard horse toil in chains and shafts, they are greatly in use. In and about the mazy winds, and through the dark arches of Bermondsey you will come across them any hour of a hard working day, each and all walking at a faster pace than is allowed by the managers of brewery studs.'

The greys and blue roans of John Mowlem and Son, builders, were used for heavy stone hauling. The cement, timber and glazier and varnish trades preferred smooth-legged horses, upstanding like the Cleveland, or with the short, cobby Norfolk cart-horse characteristics. The latter trotted well under a medium load and lighter still were the beautiful, active horses of the pantechnicon vans, capable of trotting home with the empty van at seven miles an hour.

Lewis Berger and Son, starch manufacturers, preferred massive greys up to 17.2 hands, and 'not falling away below the knee as is sometimes seen in very heavy greys' as Dykes observed. Greys found a place in fire engines, the colour being conspicuous and apparently more fortunate than others in obtaining a clear road.

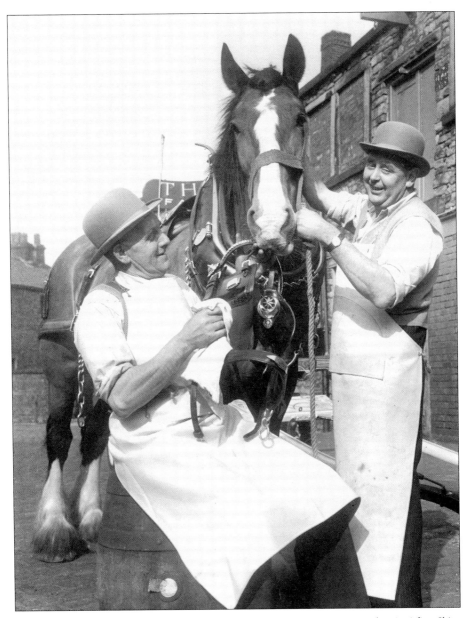

Happy horsemen. Harry Crossland and head horseman Bill Sycamore prepare Thwaites' first Shire Dan for his 1960 initiation. (Daniel Thwaites plc)

One type of working horse was always black, though it seldom comprised true heavies. Though coal horses were often black or dark bays, matching the coalman's clothes, the real 'black brigade' of London streets was made up of funeral horses. Job-masters specialised in the requisite type of horse just as others catered for pleasure outings or goods deliveries.

One stable on the East Road housed 80 Flemish horses, big, black and good-natured. A peculiarity here was that every horse was named after the celebrity, ancient or contemporary, most talked of at the time of his purchase, so General Booth, Huxley, Dickens and John Knox shared the same stable. An odd superstition arose from the use of church or chapel dignitaries' names. 'All the horses named after that kind of person go wrong somehow,' said the horsekeeper.

Mr Dotteridge, who headed a funeral firm, declared himself to be 'not a horsey man', yet he could assess a horse's nature by the peculiar glance it gave when looking round at him. He liked Roman noses, 'I never knew a horse with a Roman nose to be ill-natured'.

Another well-documented superstition was that the black horses became unhappy and restless if a coloured horse was stabled amongst them. If the same owner dealt in the different kinds, separate stables were used. The black funeral horses were tall, about 16 hands, and weighed 12 to 13 cwt. No great strength was needed, but an equable disposition combined with smartness was required.

Before British Rail cloaked stimulating rivalries under its universal umbrella, railway companies took special pride in selecting their own stamp and colour of horses. Glasgow draymen differed from London breweries in their horse types, favouring a muscular and more active, if not such a weighty, specimen. While the best London dray horses scaled 18 to 21 cwt, Glasgow's were 16 to 18 cwt. The latter were used singly, hauling 3½ tons including the vehicle, while a London pair would move 5 tons and more. Liverpool had some of the best and heaviest, and the record pull with Shires was made there. There is a Liverpool bit and a Liverpool shoe.

EDWARD HART, *THE BOOK OF THE HEAVY HORSE*, 1986

Launching the Lifeboats

Throughout the late 1880s until the mid-1920s and early 1930s the sail and row lifeboats of the RNLI were launched and recovered by large teams of horses. In the main the RNLI owned very few horses – the Institution relied on local farmers to muster the teams for the launch. From these years came some epic stories, like the Lynmouth Porlock launch of 1898 and the terrible tragedies, such as the Hunstanton incident of 1897, both related here.

Appledore No 2 is launched after arriving at the station.

The lifeboats from the early part of the century were 30–5 ft long and weighed 20–4 tons. They were rowed and sailed and the horses used to launch and recover them were usually ridden postillion fashion. The eight- or ten-horse teams would be pulling, all be it over a short distance, something up to 28–30 tons because the weight of the trolley has to be included, as well as the drag of wet sand. The load on each horse was considerable.

The last horses used for launch and recovery came to the end of their work in 1936 at Wells in Norfolk. This left only two horses in the RNLI service at Hastings, which turned a capstain (probably more familiar to most readers as a horse gear or gin) to winch the boat up the beach. This was soon replaced by an electric winch.

From 1920 mechanization rapidly took over as crawler tractors became more popular for launching and through the 1930s the farmers who supplied the horses were also gradually changing over to tractors.

DAVID BAKEWELL, *HEAVY HORSE WORLD*, 1987

Volunteers in Action

On the evening of Thursday 12 January 1899 a telegraph message was received at Lynmouth in North Devon that a ship was in distress in Porlock Bay and was in immediate danger of running ashore. Seas were sweeping across Lynmouth harbour and over the seafront, and after some discussion it was agreed that the Lynmouth lifeboat could not be launched.

Lynmouth and Porlock are separated by Countisbury Hill with a gradient of one in four and a half, a long stretch of open moor and then Porlock Hill, where the descent is in places almost sheer. The coxswain of the Lynmouth lifeboat suggested to the local vicar, who was also honorary secretary of the lifeboat station, that an attempt should be made to transport the lifeboat overland to Porlock. The vicar agreed.

The people of Lynmouth turned out in large numbers. Horses were produced from various quarters, one farmer from Lynton providing more than a dozen. The lifeboat signalman was sent ahead in charge of a small party equipped with pick-axes and shovels to widen the road where necessary. Flat wooden skids were taken by cart. Such light as there was came from flares and oil lanterns. A full gale was blowing from the west-north-west.

With the horses pulling and people pushing, the lifeboat on her carriage was slowly brought to the top of Countisbury Hill. A wheel then came off the carriage. This was put on again and a spare linchpin was fitted. On the most exposed part of Exmoor the road was found to be too narrow for the lifeboat to pass through on her carriage. The lifeboat was therefore dragged along on skids, and after some gateposts had been broken down the carriage was taken over the open moor to rejoin the lifeboat farther along the road.

In the descent down Porlock Hill the greatest danger was that the lifeboat would slip off her carriage. With the use of drag-ropes and safety chains this

The self-righting lifeboat *Charley Lloyd*, built in 1871, was 33 ft by 8 ft with ten oars.

danger was averted, but near the bottom of the hill the road was again found to be too narrow for lifeboat and carriage. To bring them through it was necessary to knock down a stone wall. It was agreed that this must be done.

An old woman living in a nearby cottage came out and asked indignantly what was happening. She had never before seen a lifeboat, but when it was explained to her why men were demolishing a wall in the middle of the night she joined enthusiastically in the work.

After a ten-and-a-half hour overland journey, without even stopping to eat, the Lynmouth crew put out in their lifeboat from Porlock and successfully escorted the 1,900 ton full-rigged ship *Forest Hall* to Barry in South Wales.

A similar overland journey conducted by horses and men took place between Whitby and Robin Hood's Bay in January 1881, with snow and ice adding to the hazards. Indeed before tractors, motorized lifeboats and radio communication were available journeys of this kind, though rarely needed, were accepted as part of the lifeboat service. When they occurred the involvement of virtually the whole local community with the lifeboat, the lifeboat crew and the purposes they served became apparent. Yet at all times this involvement remained, as it remains today, latent at least in many coastal towns and villages. It is one of the reasons why the lifeboat service continues to be a voluntary one.

DAVID BAKEWELL, 1987

One of the Greatest of the 'Big Teams'

Reginald Ottley had been travelling across inland Australia on a big bay riding horse, to escape from an area flooded by six weeks of constant rain.

As he reached the point where the bridge should have been, he found a table-top waggon and 14 tons of wool, bogged down. It was in the charge of 'Yacka', an experienced bushman. Its own eighteen horses and eighteen from another waggon in the convoy of four had failed to move it. So the teams from all the waggons, seventy-six horses in all, were being yoked to it; and being yoked more than belly deep in swirling, muddy flood waters.

'Yacka' arranged them the way he wanted: a pair of his own, then several pairs of the other teamsters' horses. Placing them in that manner, he had horses that knew his voice all along the great team. Waggon teams are driven by voice, not with reins.

The horses became restless. They wanted to swing their rumps to the rain. We had to squeeze in between them to get to their heads. Some lashed out, others bumped us with their ribs. No team horse is ever fully broken; he is only taught to lead, and have a collar, blinkers and chains slipped on him. For the rest, he is left pretty much to himself – never has his feet picked up, or anything like that. Shoes are an unknown quantity.

Eventually the huge team was lined up, and the leaders yoked. 'Yacka's' leaders were a gelding named Toby and a mare, Bonny. Both were massive, in a raw-boned way. 'Yacka' told them to ease up, and in so doing stretched out the team until, inch by inch, every horse was standing straight, settled into his collar.

Then 'Yacka's' voice boomed again. 'Toby! Bonny! Wedge up there. Wedge up there, or I'll dust your hides.' Slowly; so slowly you could see him twitch with the strain, Toby heaved into his collar. Bonny did the same. Behind them, one after the other, the rest of the team dipped their heads. Hoof by sucking hoof, they strained forward.

The waggon began to roll, surging through the flood, with a crest on its prow. 'Yacka' kept the team going.

His voice urged them; coaxed them; swore at them. But you could feel his love for the horses, straining under his urging. Then, suddenly, the waggon

Timber Hauling, by Nathaniel Hughes John Baird (1865–1936). Sally Mitchell writes of the Roxburghshire-born artist: 'He favoured heavy horses . . . and his work displays a tremendous feel for sunlight and the elements. His horses are powerful and realistic.' (Sally Mitchell Prints)

rolled freely. It had reached hard ground, and its weight was nothing for the great team. Pounding through the water, they almost bolted. But 'Yacka's' great voice held them, eased them down slowly. Prick-eared under the calling, Toby and Bonny eased their pulling. The team behind them slackened off, too, without tangling their chains.

Such stories are a tribute to the great lead horses, of Shires and other breeds, that first cultivated the New World. They have no memorials. Yet without their understanding and intelligent reactions, the massed power behind them would have been useless. I hope some fellow writer in those wide countries can set down their feats, before they are lost and buried by the hundred-horse power, soul-less tractor.

REGINALD L. OTTLEY, *THE LISTENER*, JUNE 1960

The Boat Horse

The boat horse worked in a different world from the other draught horses. His world was that of the towpath, and he was specially trained for that work. His master also lived in a different world from his neighbours and, like his horse, once brought into the world of the canals seldom ventured far away from it. His work, his tradition and his ways of living were all centred on the canals, and for this reason it is appropriate to treat his horse, the boat horse, separately from the other draught horses.

The boat horse was a special kind of horse, and yet it would be difficult to describe him. It would have been a rare sight to see an aristocrat of the heavy draught breeds, a pure Shire, Clydesdale or Suffolk in the harness of a boat horse. A boater was limited in height to 15.3 hands, no higher, because of the heights of the bridges along the towpaths. He had to be able to pass under these bridges without discomfort. The tallest ones learnt to hold their heads to one side to avoid having their ears rubbed raw, especially when negotiating the few tunnels which were provided with towpaths.

The boater had to be strong. A good boat horse could shift 50 tons on a good canal, one with a properly dredged channel and a well maintained tow-path. But it was not just strength alone. The horse had to be trained to move the load in easy stages. Once the boat was moving the job of keeping it going was much easier. It was estimated in 1810 that one horse and three men could move as much by barge as sixty horses and ten men could carry by wagon on the roads. The boater had also to be relied on to pull steadily for long hours. A horse could pull a loaded narrow boat at 2 m.p.h. and two together at 1½ m.p.h. Empty they could pull them at 3 m.p.h. and 2½ m.p.h. respectively. Said Alf Edwards, of Wolverhampton, 'The horses had to work hard and very long hours. We would keep them going as long as we could. The one horse would pull the boat all the way from Wolverhampton to Ellesmere Port. But in fourteen years of working this route we only ever had four different horses.'

The half-legged horse was the most popular type in use as a boater.

Canal companies supplied horses and harness to work their own boats, but there was also an independent boatman who owned his own boat and his horse and harness. He was known as a 'number one', and took an extra pride in his turn-out. Jack James was a number one and was brought up on the 'bread and lard' cut – the Oxford Canal. 'At certain places along the canal we could buy horses, usually from the didikaies. Often we would do a straight swop.' To a number one the horse came before the rest of the family, even when times were hard, simply because it was the horse that earned them their living. The horse, as head of the family, would be fed and bedded down at night before either the boatman or his family.

TERRY KEEGAN, *THE HEAVY HORSE: ITS HARNESS AND HARNESS DECORATION*, 1973

Old Warrior

We have put hours of effort into schooling the young carthorse Prince. He ploughs faultlessly, ambles along with the heavy ribbed roller, draws the seed drill. But when we harnessed him to the grass clipper he went little short of berserk. He bucked, kicked, struck out wildly with all four legs and only with the greatest of difficulty did we prevent him hauling the clipper, and his mate, Blue, through the hedge and into the ditch.

The trouble with cutting grass for making hay is that there is no choice in the matter: when it has to be done, it has to be done. I too had waited for my weather window to give perfect conditions and I could not be let down by an unwilling young soldier. I looked at Derek, and we clearly had the same thought running through our minds. Prince was unhitched and led back to the stable in shame, and I sprinted to the meadow to catch old Star.

Star, of course, is retired; he has been at grass since the spring and clearly enjoys it. He has buttercups to sniff, long grass to chew and the pleasant sight of everyone working hard, apart from him. We did not have time to feed him. It was as if we had taken a snoozing Chelsea pensioner straight from his deckchair on the beach and put him in the driving seat of a front-line tank. Yet one word of command from me and Star stepped forward with the verve and agility of a young 'un.

He did not falter. He and Blue stepped out, side by side, advancing round the field, scything through the long grass and letting it be no hindrance to their relentless march.

Harrowing, by John Trickett. A contemporary picture of a traditional heavy horse scene. Less skilled than ploughing, the work can be harder physically; there are no plough stilts to lean on! (Sally Mitchell Prints)

What an old soldier that horse is. Unlike the best armies, he did not even have a full stomach on which to march, nor did he have any shoes, for the farrier removed them when I decided he had had his day. Blue, ten years younger, was soon in a sweat; but not old Star. He faced the enemy and, without even any boots on his feet, marched steadily forward to victory. He is a hero.

When the sun eventually sets over these few acres, we shall remember him.

PAUL HEINEY, *THE TIMES*, 18 JUNE 1994

Novice Ploughman

It was not the first rigg I had set, but usually I followed the Boss after his horses had drawn a mark as if by rule across the dull gold stubble.

I measured my 22 yards from the last rigg. ('Your yards are 4 feet', the Boss was wont to say.) I tied a rather grubby handkerchief in the hedge as marker at one end, and set a light pole halfway down the field.

Blossom and Bonnie turned in at the appropriate mark on the headland, and I squinted up the field, noting with satisfaction that centre pole and handkerchief were dead in line.

Immediately above that far hedge was a bank of persil-white cloud, and rising from it a thin plume of cloud, like an umpire's index finger signalling 'Out!'.

To my youthful imagination that pillar of cloud was placed there providentially, for my cloth was barely discernible. We set off. Blossom and Bonnie pushed over the centre pole and continued making the furrow. My eye was held by that glistening pencil of cloud; no need to bother about an old handkerchief. The air was still, with scarcely a brown leaf stirring, and all would be well.

The shining plough point emerged from the headland as the team swung out. My first indication of doom came when I saw the grey wisp of handkerchief nestling 8 yards to my left. I hardly dare look round. When I did, I found the second half of the rigg in a beautifully symmetrical curve.

Until then I had not realized that air conditions at ground level could be vastly different from a few hundred feet up. My beckoning pillar had drifted slowly, and thrown all my efforts awry.

What to do now? Perhaps I could turn the furrow back, reset the rigg and plough in the scar, but it was not to be. My employer had arrived with the 'ten o'clocks'. He stood on the headland and looked down the line. Usually ever ready with a merry quip at the expense of learner ploughmen, on this occasion the Boss was speechless.

EDWARD HART, 1970

The Ploughing Lesson

I watched with envy Carter come,
pace out his 'land' and set the markers up,
leaving his team to stand, patient by the
pool beneath sun gilded elms.
I saw him hang his 'kerchief, on the face
of the shadowed wood and turn his back
upon its wind wracked shaking.
As I bent to my picking of stones,
he called me, 'Wanna plough, Boy?'
'Oh yes!' I shouted.
'Then let me set
up my ridge and ye shall,' he laughed.
Small, uncertain figure, I stood at the
plough's tail.

'Take 'old the lines an' feel their mouths,'
said Carter. 'Right?' I nodded. 'Ketch 'old
the 'andles.' I did so. 'See me mark?'
'Yes Carter,' I said. 'Now listen well.
Let the 'osses go easy. They do know
better than thee. Jest look ter mark
an' never look back . . .
'Right lad. Give 'em the word an' 'old tight!'
'Bonny! Captain!' I chirruped.
An ear twitched, a head tossed, but nothing else.
'Damnee Boy' roared Carter. 'Yer not
a bloody cricket on the hearth!
Tell them!'
'Get up!' I yelled and nearly lost
both shoulders and the skidding plough.
Then I was ploughing, part of a whole:
proud team of horses, plume nodding,
brass bedecked, deliberate stepping and
the living, lissom, plough.
Smelling the new found earth and
hearing it kiss the mirrored breast as it
turned to lie again, new, level and upended.
Blur of the shadowed wood became branches
and Carter's 'kerchief waving.
Ten foot high, I turned to see the work
behind me and in that moment hit a mountain.
All hell let loose, plough bucking and rearing
like a steer. A handle drove into my gut.
In panic I yelled to nothingness.
'I can't do it!' and felt Carter's
horny hands around my hands.
'Nay lad, an' yer never will, until ye learn
ter do as yer telt. An' kip yer eye
upon the mark.
Now plough. The light is goin' fast,
and we must loose out at the furrows
end and look fer home.'

DAVID B. NIXON, *PICTURES ON A WALL*, 1983

nine

Showing and Decorations

The show ground is where most people meet the modern heavy horse. Classes there are in two main parts. In-hand or breed (halter classes in Australia and North America) consist of individual animals parading before the judge, who assesses them on conformation and breed points. In the turnout classes, the horses haul a vehicle and number from one (Single) through two to six or very occasionally eight. Three- and four-horse teams may be combined in one class, although recent excitingly increased numbers have resulted in separate classes at the bigger shows.

Two horses are usually driven side by side (Pair) but one may lead the other (Tandem). The tandem is spectacular but difficult; much depends on a good leader. Horses are gregarious animals and, while two perform happily side by side, one out in front on its own is less easy to control.

The same applies in the 'threes'. Here the formation is generally a Unicorn, with one leader and two at the wheel, either in shafts or with a pole between them. The alternative is the 'Pick Axe', with two horses in front and one between the shafts. Three abreast is another hitch, used during the 'eighties and early 'nineties by Noel Abel's pantechnicon for furniture haulage. It is also possible to yoke three horses in line, known as a 'random'. This hitch can only be used at the walk, and is consequently at a disadvantage when other teams are trotting.

The four-horse team is hitched two and two. Such turnouts are expensive in terms of transport and man power. Yet they are such crowd pullers that shows offer grants to help exhibitors compete in what would otherwise be an exercise beyond most private pockets.

The 'six' is the pinnacle of North America horsemanship. To see those massive six-horse teams entering Toronto Winter Fair's arena through its narrow arch at a fast trot makes crossing the Atlantic worthwhile. Just as the heavy horse revival spread from North America to Britain, so the 'six' is becoming a major part of our summer scene.

All these horses are neatly decorated and braided, but separate classes for Best Decorated are another aspect.

A good specimen of a heavy of any breed can carry an immense weight and variety of decorations. Though they vary from north to south, all reflect a specialist art in which the value of the horse matters less than in most in-hand classes.

We follow the early development and burgeoning popularity of horse brasses, and hear from the men who plait manes and tails and add floral and woollen decorations.

How to Show a Shire

A few remarks on the above subject will not come amiss, at least to the uninitiated, for it is tolerably certain that, other things being equal, the candidate for honours which makes the best show when it is actually before the judges stands the first chance of securing the honours.

It must not be expected that a colt can be fetched out of a grass field one day and trained well enough to show himself off creditably in the ring the next; and a rough raw colt makes both itself and its groom look small. Training properly takes time and patience, and it is best to begin early with the process, from birth for choice. The lessons need not, and certainly should not, be either long or severe at the

Major amuses HM The Queen by bowing during her Shire Horse Society Presidential year, 1977. (Daniel Thwaites plc)

outset, but just enough to teach the youngster what is required of him. When teaching horses to stand at 'attention' they should not be made to stretch themselves out as if they were wanted to reach from one side of the ring to the other, neither should they be allowed to stand like an elephant on a tub. They should be taught to stand squarely on all fours in a becoming and businesslike way. The best place for the groom when a horse is wanted to stand still is exactly in front and facing the animal. The rein is usually gripped about a foot from the head. Mares can often be allowed a little more 'head,' but with stallions it may be better to take hold close to the bit, always remembering to have the loop end of the rein in the palm, in case he suddenly rears or plunges. The leader should 'go with his horse,' or keep step with him, but need not 'pick up' in such a manner as to make it appear to bystanders that he is trying to make up for the shortcomings of his horse.

Both horse and man want to practise the performance in the home paddock a good many times before perfection can be reached, and certainly a little time thus spent is better than making a bad show when the critical moment arrives that they are both called out to exhibit themselves before a crowd of critics.

A.J. FROST, *THE SHIRE HORSE IN PEACE AND WAR*, 1915

Enoch at the Door

Louise Jackson was alone in the house on a bleak February afternoon, and it was getting dark. Her husband had been away since Monday and she thought of the sixteen rooms and the strange noises a place makes in the night.

Was there anything horrible outside? What if a face appeared at a window? She started to close the downstairs shutters.

Suddenly there was tremendous hammering at the door. She froze with terror. Silence. Then it started again, but was succeeded by a voice. 'Open up, missus, open up! We've won London!'

It was Enoch Bostock, her husband's boss, excited as a schoolboy. His yearling filly Old House Mimic's Starlight had been awarded first prize at the Shire Show. He had to tell someone quick, so he called on William's wife at Tocil Farm.

The Bostocks, from time immemorial, had farmed in Staffordshire and neighbouring counties. If anyone asked Enoch how long that had really been so, he would say 'I think it must have been since the world began'.

For our purposes, the middle years of Victoria's reign will do. They were keeping good dray stallions then, such as Tice Em and Bang-Up. Three Bostock brothers became famous names in the circus. Two of their cousins, George and his brother John, farmed at Baginton, near Coventry, but there was a row when one told the other that he was thinking of buying a certain farm and the other slipped off and bought it for himself. As happens so often, the family row became a feud.

George went off to farm in Cheshire and later came back to the Kenilworth area where in due course he prospered and had several farms. One of his nine children was Enoch, born in 1878, who took over the smallest farm when he was fifteen and was therefore sufficiently experienced to move to Gibbett Hill at twenty-one. He joined the Shire Horse Society in 1902, and now it was 1933. He owned twenty acres and a few houses, and rented three large farms. He set his face against buying, because land could only depreciate. So he put his money into stocks and shares, and was a director of Coventry Dairy.

Hammering on the door like that was not typical at all of Mr Bostock. Only a first prize in London could make him do it. There was no question of alcoholic celebrations, either. He hardly drank anything since, at the age of sixteen, someone had given him a lot of smooth parsnip wine (1872 vintage in 1894) which put him to bed for a week.

A character in the thirties, he lived to be an anachronism. In the family of nine, three had married and three were old maids keeping house, one house each, for the three old bachelors. He was one of these. He smoked his daily three ounces of tobacco, but a glass of beer and a pork pie had always sufficed as food and drink at a show, even if he had the champion.

He was addicted to flannel shirts without a collar. He had once tried to replace his old overcoat, and the shop was unsuccessfully ransacked to find one like he had bought there forty years before.

He had also failed to discover a new hat. 'I bought this one in Leamington thirty years ago and I ought to buy another, but I can't find one like it. In any case, I've grown fond of it .' His suit, when he had to wear one, was even older. He remained ever faithful to that which he had bought, with drainpipe legs, as a young man. He wore heavy boots and always had his knobbly stick.

At his death on 16 October 1956, aged 78, three years after handing over to a nephew, he was worth £100,000, a useful sum then for a man who had set his face against the folly of buying land. When the farms at last became the site of Warwick University, his policy of course might have been questioned, but it was too late then.

KEITH CHIVERS, *HEAVY HORSE & DRIVING*, MARCH/APRIL 1982

*London Harness Horse Parade
(Centenary 1985)*

For thirty years we've always made our way
on every Easter Monday holiday.
To Regents Park and there see splendidly displayed
Big entries in the harness horse parade.

The 'turn-outs' one by one arrive
And vary greatly: likewise they who drive.
All those who thought the draught-horse was abolished
Will find him here with trappings highly polished.

Hackney and Shetland, cob and mule and donkey
A costermonger's vivid cart and monkey.
Gay Easter bonnets here and there we see
Plus carriages of great antiquity.

The gentle giants draw the heavier carts
They have a splendid patience in their hearts.
The drivers prize their bright rosettes and brasses.
Presented at the second time they pass us.

And at the last the mounted police appear
I pay them tribute – good to have you here!
I call the multitude to silence, then to pray,
and with God's blessing send them on their way.

REVD PHILIP WRIGHT, *RUSTIC RHYMES*, 1985

A Ploughing Match

But back to 'once upon a time.' I had ridden my bike to North Cave to a ploughing match. The pairs of horses were arriving yoked to wagons bringing their ploughs, which were unloaded and taken up to their numbered pegs on the headland. Meantime the horses had their final grooming and their manes and tails were plaited up. There were two types of plaiting mainly used: the ordinary three plait and the rig plait, which took longer to do with the hair parted and twisted into two separate rows. The brass bells would be fastened on the top of the headband, the face brasses and martingales. After a final polish, the horse would be ready to be yoked to the plough.

Sometimes the pair of horses would be judged for the smartest turnout, sometimes not, but whatever the conditions the ploughman never took a pair of young horses. It was always his own pair, probably a pair that he had worked for years.

The horses were put to the plough, with traces that had been polished until they shone by putting them into a bag of wheat straw tied by each corner to the wheel of a wagon. Each turn of the wheel sent the chains turning and twisting all the way to the station or mill. One journey worked wonders with a set of traces.

Autumn means bare stubbles . . . and ploughing matches.

The backbands were on, the traces fastened, the cobbletree and swingletrees were checked, the traces hooked on, and now the plough was set up to the correct width and depth of furrow. Is it nine inches wide and four deep, or is it eight wide and five deep? The stewards will tell him.

The ploughman has been told the number he has drawn when he arrived. Each competitor draws his starting point so he has had time to check what the land is like, but there is no walking across on his piece to plough. He views it from the ends only. There are no bookies shouting the odds, just a few quiet bets amongst the onlookers between themselves, because each man will be fancied.

The depth and width were set, the coulter clean and sharp, the slape clean and shiny, a good sock – one that has had a day's use, just to take the rough edges off it and make it shine. There must be no risk of any soil sticking to any part; it can leave a nasty scar on the face of the turned-up furrow and lose him points.

Jack and Jenny were finally yoked up, with the strings that the ploughman drives them with tied from bit to hand, one to nearside and one to offside. Jenny is his furrow horse; she has always been his furrow horse. It's stubble field, so all the ploughmen know what sort of a rig to make. A rig on stubble land is made by turning the first furrow to the right and coming back anti-clockwise throwing the next furrow away from it.

Right – our man gets his pair set straight, his eyes on his marker on the other side. The moment comes. 'Gee up Jack, Jenny.' He sets a small object such as a stone or anything sticking up in a direct line for his distant mark; not a sound except for a very quiet 'Woave Jack' or gentle 'Gee back, Jenny.' His guiding strings will not be used. A good ploughman guided his horses by gentle commands: to go left was 'woave,' to go right was 'gee back.'

A few minutes later he is at the far side and looks back; perfect, straight as a die, not an inch out. He turns his pair round for to throw the second furrow out. 'Woave Jack, woave Jenny' turns them anti-clockwise for this time only to face the return journey, and this is where he knows one slip or a small stone wedged between his coulter point and the plough sock could lose him points for tidiness.

He has to turn his next furrow away from the first one and his coulter point has to cut exactly on the line that it cut on the first run. The horse placings were now reversed. Jenny, used to being the furrow, was now on the land and Jack in the furrow. Jenny was well trained. She would be content to be there, but sometimes a 'furrow' horse would be gently pushing its way back into the furrow, causing that little loss of concentration by the ploughman by his having to keep calling 'gee back' to keep it in its right place.

Back to the·starting point, the two furrows thrown out, perfect! Now to the second act, turning one of the thrown-out furrows back, plus a similar sized one from underneath. So, it's turn round again. Jenny back in the furrow, landwheel and furrow wheel to be adjusted again. They must be exactly right. 'Gee up.' Off again, turn round, right wheel this time, back to the starting point leaving behind a perfectly shaped and straight rig. The two double furrows are now set side by side and two empty furrows for the next turns to plough into. The judges have checked. He now only has to plough a stated number of turns, keep his furrow absolutely straight and he could be the winner.

HARRY REFFOLD, *PIE FOR BREAKFAST*, 1984

Heavy Charm of the Soft-shoe Shuffle

Outside the Wembley Arena, a ticket tout was calling 'Who wants one?' I watched him for ten minutes: me under my umbrella, he under his. Trade was non-existent. Inside, on the first floor where there is a burger bar, a champagne bar, a spuds-and-beer bar and a high-class purveyor of Belgian chocolates, none of which contained crystalized ginger, I encountered Mr Coomes. His trade was negligible also.

Coomes is a bookmaker. In 1986 he gave me 12–1 against Rosie Barnes winning the by-election in Greenwich, since when I have had considerable affection for him.

Now the man was taking bets on the outcome of the Radiol Senior Newcomers championship at the Horse of the Year Show: even money Penwood Fleetway through to 14–1 the outsiders. The nearest and dearest of owners, riders and stable lads supported their fancies with fivers. I enquired about the volume of business; he opined that one must not grumble.

An elder of equestrianism came by, shook my hand, reminded me of the halcyon days when a 14.2 pony called Stroller won the grand prix, became TV personality of the year and was nearly elected rector of Aberdeen University. He peered at the half-empty hall and said: 'Things are not good.'

The voice over the Tannoy announced that six of the nineteen horses had jumped clear rounds, that there would be a jump-off. Professor Higgins would have identified the accent at once: Wellington, Sandhurst, Army, Home Counties. It was the voice that used to tell me to fasten my seat-belt when I had an Austin Maestro which talked.

With little to lose, now might be the time to hand the microphone to a Rastafarian.

The favourite took the £180 prize for senior newcomers – will probably be aimed at junior veterans next – and it was time for what I consider to be the very best event of the week, the Osborne Refrigeration Musical Drive of the Heavy Horses.

As the sponsors deserve praise let me explain that Osborne make ozone-friendly commercial refrigerators in Bognor Regis; were I in the market for such products, I should go nowhere else.

The six pairs of Shires, largest and heaviest of all horses, came into the arena drawing harrows, driven by men dressed in red dustcoats and brown stove-pipe hats which make them look like Dickensian bailiffs.

As they paraded around the ring it was difficult not to empathise with the predicament of Mr Norris, our beleaguered minister of transport.

Did we not lose our hearts to the beauty of Malt and Barley from Thwaites Brewery in Blackburn; then become enamoured of the pulchritude of the black Wandles, Selwyn and Charlton, from Young's in Wandsworth . . . and be captivated by the grey grandeur of Hengist and Hector from Paddock Wood, even while flirting with the sublime splendour of Courage's Brookfield Tim and King and the symmetrical comeliness of Samson and Majestic exhibited by Löwenbräu?

Norris took twenty years. It took us ten minutes to run the gamut of these emotions, with time to catch our breath at the gorgeousness of Royal and Sovereign from the Whitbread Hop Farm.

As we in the auditorium basked in contentment, the band seated on an elevated platform and attended by an enthusiastic pigeon, played martial music and the stirring airs beloved by those who annually bankrupt themselves to buy seats for the last night of the Proms at the Albert Hall.

Dray King enjoys a pint with Patrick Flood. (Daniel Thwaites plc)

Did the horses dance to the music – or was it the conductor who orchestrated his men to accompany the soft-shoe shuffle of 12 tonnes of horseflesh?

The lights dimmed and four dozen hooves swathed in white fleece seemed to stamp in harmony to the overture to William Tell, sway to There'll Always Be An England.

The twelve geldings with red plumes on their heads and coloured ribbons attached to their tails moved with the dignity, grace and joy that is so sadly missing among the contestants of *Come Dancing*. It is to the great credit of the organizers that for the duration of the musical drive there was no commentary. We – and especially us in the area reserved for foreign owners, where I sat between a woman from Tunbridge Wells and two Yorkshiremen – watched in silent admiration. When it was all done, when the last pair of Suffolk Punches left the arena, our applause was fervent and sustained.

As apprentice farriers from the Warwickshire College raced into the ring to set up obstacles for the Spillers Pony Club Mounted Games it was the consensus of the crowd that regardless of the standing of the Horse of the Year Show, there is something quite exceptionally uplifting about the parade of the descendants of our great, medieval war horses.

CLEMENT FREUD, *THE TIMES*, 8 OCTOBER 1993

Aristocrat Takes Title

From a record entry of 233 animals Ladbrook Aristocrat, a black five-year-old stallion was pulled out of a high quality final line-up to take the supreme male championship at the National Shire Horse Show at Peterborough last weekend.

Paraded by A.W. Lewis of Solihull, he is a son of Ladbrook Invader and out of the Alneland Delegate daughter Ladbrook Gillian.

Another black stallion, Tom Moss's (Congleton) Metheringham Joseph stood reserve overall in the male championship. Bred by G. Robinson, this four-year-old is by Hainton Jim out of a Tremoelgoch mare by Grangewood Bengie.

The Hillmoor Enterprise son Royston Enterprise from John C. Stubbs at Ashbourne took the junior male ticket. He was bred by R.B. Hart, of Haverfordwest, and is out of a Crossfield Supreme-sired mare.

Leading the geldings was Ty Fry Hiawatha, a Woodhouse Pioneer son from W.S. Innes, of Anglesey, with the brown 1977-bred Whitley Superstar, by Wood house Footprint, in reserve. He was paraded by A.W. Wright, of Warrington.

The seasoned campaigner Jim's Lucky Charm headed a good entry of females and collected the championship for her owners J.B. Cooke of Spalding. By Hillmoor Enterprise this bay five-year-old is out of a mare by Lymm Sovereign.

The reserve best mare was Treuddyn Duchess, a dark bay from J. and E. Salt (Uttoxeter). This two-year-old by Quixhill Masterpiece was out of an Edingale

Arthur Lewis, one of the band who kept the heavy horse alive when all seemed lost, seen here at the Royal Show with his influential stallion, Ladbrook Aristocrat.

158

Selector mare and bred by J.W. Read, of Mold. She also took both junior female titles.

Topping the yearlings was Royston Louise from C.C. Etches of Ashbourne. By Royston Harold she is out of a mare by Carr Coming King.

ANON., FARMERS' GUARDIAN, 1980

William Guthrie, Ploughing Expert

Willie Guthrie, known throughout the length and breadth of Great Britain, having coached many ploughmen in his time, was one of the ploughing experts at Ransomes, the famous English ploughmakers. This was a typical abode of a ploughman. Along one side of the room were his many trophies and a small-scale model of a plough given to him by the blacksmith who made it and beside whose forge Willie had sat as a schoolboy the while admiringly and carefully polishing this precious miniature. In pride of place beside the lawn stood an old horse plough still in first class condition and painted like new. It was the plough Willie first guided behind a pair of Clydesdales at the early age of ten years. This and two other horse ploughs in mint condition are ever constant reminders of a profession about which the famous Scottish bard, Robert Burns, declared

> Of all the trades that I do ken,
> Commend me to the ploughman.

ALFRED HALL, PLOUGHMAN'S PROGRESS, 1992

Henry Pollard Judges the National Shire Shows

Henry Pollard was very proud after being presented to H.R.H. Princess Anne at the Peterborough Show to be asked by her what points he looks for when judging Shire horses.

First look at the feet, he told her, if you haven't got a good foot you haven't got a good horse.
There should be plenty of width at the heel.
The frog should be level with the ground.
Good pastern.
Plenty of good flat bone.
Nice straight silky feather.
Good forearm.
Good width under the chest – you should be able to put a bowler hat between the front legs under the chest.

Long lean head.

Eyes well set and docile in expression, (Wall eyes are unacceptable).

Slight roman nose.

Neck slightly arched.

Short back with plenty of depth behind the shoulder giving plenty of heart room.

Good clean firm hocks.

Tail placed high – Henry said 'When a horse is standing correctly you should be able to tip water over its tail and the falling water should just touch the tip of its hoof.'

He further said that if it is strong in the tail it would be strong in the back, the stronger the back, the greater the resistance to having its tail raised.

The horse must be in good condition and take the judge's eye.

It should use its hocks well.

When it picks up its front foot the hind one should drop in its place.

Bay View Shirley is without doubt Henry's pride and joy, he found the black filly foal after a search that took him over a thousand miles visiting shows and

This evocative picture of horse, groom and auctioneer has been repeated thousands of times since horses first worked the land. (Sally Mitchell Prints)

sales. To date Shirley has won one hundred and forty nine championships, forty seven of which have been for Supreme Champion over all other breeds in show and she has won five hundred and seventy nine first prizes. (It is possible to enter the same horse in two or three classes which is why Shirley has won as many as three first prizes and the championship and supreme championship at one show.)

Shirley has had two foals – the first a colt was sold locally and is now gelded, the second, a filly Bay View Genie, was sold to Mr Smrt in America and hopefully she is in foal again due early next spring.

Ribwood Blossom to date has won thirty eight championships and her foal Bay View Melody has won one and has yet to be beaten in the foal class. A yearling Marr Charlotte has won a great many first prizes and two championships.

Henry is showing all four of these Shires this season.

HENRY POLLARD, 1984

Place in Shire History for Landcliffe Laura

Ringside judges at Wembley watched a fascinating morning preliminary session with no clear idea of the eventual winner. Some thought that Bedfords' Landcliffe Laura might not add to her triple crown, but the man in the middle, Mr Henry Pollard from Cornwall, decided otherwise.

When Laura gave her final display under the Wembley spotlight, her spirited style set the seal on a splendid season.

'Laura rises to the occasion' said Walter Bedford, who took the winning evening stint following brother Paul's capable morning showing. The dark bay nine-year-old was 15 weeks in-foal to Deighton Bomber as she entered the annals of all-time famous Shire winners. Laura had won four female championships at the Peterborough Spring Show, two at Newark, two at the Great Yorkshire, and three at the East of England.

The aforementioned ringside judges at this Dubonnet Red Shire Horse of the Year championship gave a great chance to G. Lloyd Owen's Tremoelgoch Lucky Charm; she had a lovely eye-catching movement. Mr Pollard placed her second, and did not regard her lack of hair adversely so late in the season.

In third place was Reg Coward's 18 hands four-year-old bay St Vincents Royale. Bred by Fred Harlock, the lovely gelding was ineligible for stallion registration, and Mr Pollard found 'nothing wrong with him in any way', but described himself as a 'mare' man.

Two horses bred by Robert Hull qualified. His own Stanley House Duchess went nicely for daughter Anne to take fourth, while David Worthington claimed fifth with Stanley House Aristocrat, an active nine-year-old proving himself as a sire.

John Etches was sixth with Royston Sally-Ann, a black three-year-old with a winning history since her foal days, and the promise of more to come. Less well known was Rhyd-y-Groes Catrin, from Devon's National Shire Horse Centre, in seventh.

Eighth place went to one of two promising colts. J.D. Joseph's Nottage Trump Card followed up his Spring Show Junior Championship by qualifying at the Bath & West, but was just too full of himself to show well under the lights. Another two-year-old colt with a future was Dothan Master Mind, already 18hh, from E.W. Roberts, Anglesey.

EDWARD HART, *HEAVY HORSE WORLD*, 1988

Decorations Will be Worn

'Where did 'ee put that there tin of brass polish, Tim?'

'Used en all, I tell 'ee! Can't you see I 'ave?'

'No, ah don't believe thee! Give they bridles another rub awver, will 'ee, just vor luck!'

All sorts of polish and every kind of saddle soap regardless of extra pence have been in demand. So has elbow-grease, but you don't have to buy that up at the shop; you spend it out of yourself. The corn-bin in the stables has been dipped into a little deeper with nobody saying 'Nay'; nose-bags have been topped up a little higher, and the result is that Prince and Duke, 'as fine and upstanding a pair as ever was, are reg'lar in the pink, if not reg'lar above theirselves' for the ploughing match.

But when the day comes, they are not the only ones. Other people have been busy with polish, soap and elbow-grease. There are a dozen teams all equally fine and upstanding, there is a brave display on all sides of brasses and buckles gleamingly polished; there are gay rosettes and ribbons in bright blues, reds, oranges and greens, and when the sun comes through – a little fitfully on this October morning – a dancing light plays also on satin skins in perfect condition rippling over the movement of muscle and sinew underneath. They are of all the colours that the horse world knows: chestnuts, dapples, sorrels, greys and duns, not to say blacks and browns with splashes of white here and there on a pair of legs, a foot or a nose.

A large and leisurely dignity surrounds them, and they move off to sounds and simple names which have been familiar to carters and plough-boys through many a generation.

King in show harness.

There are Prince and Duke already introduced, there are several Captains, and one or two Majors. Turpin and Punch are a pair of greys, Champion and Boxer, light chestnuts, while Voi-lets, Blossoms, Smoilers and Di-monds come as nice broad vowels off the country tongue.

In the lee of the hedge-row at which Turpin and Punch snatch a quick nibble as they turn the plough, a couple of young ploughmen's wives have camped with babies and children to mind the nose-bags and other gear of their menfolk.

Here and there among the little groups of onlookers are past and present masters of the whole art of ploughing, taking a busman's holiday; tolerant but critical. Across their chests, or a little lower, massive chains anchor their best waistcoats to their watches, or perhaps it should be the other way about. They have the tanned clear skin and clear gaze of out-of-doors, with whiskers cut in various old-time modes. An ancient nearing ninety sports a gay neckcloth, but otherwise is dressed in sober black; a short-tailed coat and trousers of a character and cut no Bond Street tailor could achieve.

Among the younger set there is no regard for tradition though; no thought of dressing for the occasion or the job. They have no use for whiskers, but run rather to mops or locks of hair requiring combs and frequent care. Somehow it doesn't seem to go with gripping plough-handles. In fact, the old school doesn't hold with these new-fangled youths, one of whom is draped in cheap plus-fours and another in dirty flannel bags.

Mr 'Affingden, who has seen more ploughing matches than anybody, is of opinion that they won't neither of 'em get no prize–

'That 'em won't! No fear of that,' says a bystander.

Mr 'Affingden turns to old William in his sober blacks.

'What do 'ee think, Grandfer?'

Old William thinks hard, but with a sly twinkle of the eye.

'They'll get nowt,' he says, 'or as near as maybe.'

* * *

Cutting across their talk comes the hum and clatter of a fussy tractor entered in another class; but still the horses go backwards and forwards, up and down – this way and that into the early afternoon. Long furrows of glistening upturned earth; brown, warm, purple and richly fragrant with promise of new life, tell of a day's outing well spent.

Farmer Coulter, whose land happened to lend itself best for the event, is a lucky man. A wide stretch of many acres of cold grey stubble has been turned for him in exhibition style.

It looks a lovely and thoroughly workmanlike sight, and the first prize has gone to the young horror in the plus-fours; the second, of course, to the one in the dirty grey flannel bags!

FRANK HART, COUNTRY LIFE, 1934

Three Horse Brasses

The Staffordshire Knot was Nabob's,
And Captain's the Crescent Moon;
The White Hart shone on Prince's Head
As they toiled in the heat of June
Leading the heavy loads of hay,
Or pulling the winter plough,
Proud heads tossing, brasses asway;
Still are those brasses now.

Side by side on an oaken beam,
Smooth with the wear of years,
They glint and glow in the firelight's gleam
Touching the heat with tears;
Awakening memories laid to sleep,

And the jingle of harness is heard
As steaming Shires drink long and deep
From the trough in the stone-flagged yard.

For the Staffordshire Knot was Nabob's,
And Captain's the Crescent Moon,
And the White Hart shone on Prince's head
Through many a far-off June.

MARION HOLDEN, *THE FIELD YEAR BOOK*, 1972

Horse-teams, Bells and Brasses

At fairs and festivals the waggons as well as the horses were often decorated; the former with ears of corn tied in bunches to the lades and ladders, the latter with bells and brasses, and their manes and tails 'ridged up' or braided with straw and ribbons. It was no rare thing for the carter to be up by four o'clock on a week-day morning, or late on Sunday night, polishing the brasses in preparation for such an event or simply because the team was to be taken out on the roads the next day.

The ornaments, as has been said, are as a rule the carter's property. There are large and small horse-bells. The former, called latten-bells, are of the size of handbells, three or four to each horse, the set making up a full, rich scale. They are fixed to the hames by a hooped rod, and being protected at top and sides by leathern flaps studded with small brass plates are known also as box-bells. Their old use was to warn on-coming traffic at night or in narrow winding lanes where it was difficult for meeting vehicles to back; they are to be found in the southern and western counties more than in the north.

The small bells, fastened on an upright ornament on the horses' heads or singly at the sides, make a constant slight tinkling or all jingle suddenly whenever a horse shakes his head. These are the head-bells; and though latten-bells are hardly ever to be seen in use at present, small bells and brasses are kept by a good many carters who take a pride in their teams – fewer now, it must be owned, in the country than in London and other large towns.

Sometimes a swinger takes the place of the head-bells, a small round plate of polished brass suspended in a brass ring, which glitters like a mirror as it swings. But what are generally called the 'brasses', or amulets, are irregular plates or discs about three inches across, in the form of some device, fastened either singly at the forehead or in a series to the broad piece of leather between the collar and the girth-strap, known as the martingale or breast-strap. These ornaments are said by antiquarians to be of very ancient origin; some supposing

An Agricultural Turnout competitor at the East of England Showground.

them to be referred to in the Bible (Judges viii. 21, 26), others considering them to have been charms against the evil eye. Among the commonest forms are the sun, moon and stars; the lotus and ox's head, and many trefoil and other shapes derived therefrom; roses, thistles, wheels, knots, trees, horsemen, horses, beasts, cocks, windmills, monograms and crests. There are brass studs and sometimes larger ornaments such as hearts, diamonds or stars, on the hame rein, and brass plates of more or less richness on the loin straps (which are purely fancy additions to the harness) and sometimes on the blinkers, though these used often to be embossed with raised or moulded shapes worked in leather – cockle-shells and such like. The edges of these pieces, and of the box-bells' covering, were often ornamentally incised or stitched.

T. HENNELL, *CHANGE IN THE FARM*, 1934

Methods of Manufacture

The earliest method of producing horse brasses in quantity was to cast them in sand. The original patterns were modelled in lead by a pattern-maker. These lead patterns were then pressed into sand filled boxes, about ten patterns to a box. Channels were formed in the sand to connect each indentation of a pattern so that the molten metal could run into each impression in turn. The rough castings were then polished to give a smooth surface. Originally this was done by clamping the brass into a vice, using two projections especially cast into the back of the brass for this purpose. The face of the tightly-held brass could then be filled and polished. After polishing, the projections were cut off and their remains can usually be seen on old cast brasses.

By the turn of the century, sanding and polishing machinery had superseded hand filing and polishing so the projections became superfluous and were removed from the patterns. The hand filing and fettling of the early cast brasses gave them a superior finish not seen on the later, mass produced ones.

Machine-stamping of brasses from the sheet metal commenced about 1880. Matthew Harvey's was one of the leading firms in this field of manufacture. The earliest method was to stamp out a blank on a 'drop stamp' machine and then for an operator to cut out the pattern, one punch at a time, using a fly press. These early stamped brasses can be recognized by the irregularities in the spacing of the design. In later years, when the fashion for horse brasses was at its height, it became economically viable for a few of the larger manufacturers to have more costly tools made which could stamp out the complete design in one hefty blow. Those later stamped brasses are recognizable by the symmetry of the design, a feature lacking in the earlier stampings.

The smaller manufacturers continued to produce brasses using the older casting methods and when the demand for heavy horse harness decorations began to dwindle after the First World War it was the production of machine stamped brasses that was to suffer most. The casting of brasses continued and later took up the renewed demand brought about by the souvenir shops.

The firm of W. Thacker and Sons of Fieldgate has recently started the manufacture of stamped brasses using some of the old dies and punches, but the old 'drop stamp' machine has been replaced by a modern power press. W. Thacker and Sons were noted for the manufacture of the smaller range of decorations, particularly those for use on the lead reins and for decorating the blinkers of the bridles and also the cart saddles. These decorations were stamped out of sheet brass using fly presses. For better quality work these used to be back-filled with molten lead. Each piece is fitted with 'shanks' as a means of attaching them to the leatherwork.

Rosettes stamped out of brass are another speciality of Thackers. These are worn on the bridle where the browband meets the cheek strap. The beehive pattern was the most common to be found on heavy horse harness.

It was into this established centre of manufacture that the horse brass was introduced by an unknown opportunist who started to make them to meet the demand for a new fashion in harness decoration.

There are many known examples of decorations used on horse harness

Decorated horses played a significant role in the rare high days and holidays of Edwardian England. (John Stone)

dating from the time when man first domesticated the wild horse and took a pride in ownership. As early man was very superstitious, the first form of decoration would appear to have been a talisman to ward off evil spirts from harming his horses. Throughout history various forms of talisman have been attached to the horse's harness – from flashing objects to ward off the 'evil eye' to passages from the scriptures hung in purses around the animals' necks to appease their owners' gods.

The pendant type horse brass, as we know it today, was introduced into this country as recently as the eighteenth century. It was probably brought here by an influx of Romanies who arrived in Britain about that time. These people were, and still are today, a very superstitious race and it is very probable that they decorated the foreheads of their horses with a shiny object to protect them from evil. Not only did they have a motive for such a decoration, but they also had the necessary skills of working in metal to produce these talismen from sheet brass.

All the earliest known horse brasses are handmade from sheet, or latten brass. They were cut out using hand tools and were often hammered into shape. One of the easiest ways of recognizing a handmade brass is by the hammer marks on the back. They are, however, very rare and are prized by collectors. The evidence for attributing the origins of horse brasses to the Romanies is the use of Romany motifs in all the early brasses – i.e. hearts, moons, stars, sunflashes etc. It was some years before our carters took up the ease of these brasses for decorating their harness and so starting off the era of horse brasses.

During the eighteenth century, the improved state of the roads led to an increased use of carriages by the gentry for their travels about the country. They started the fashion of decorating the horse harness with family crests, at first worked in silver and later in nickel, or white metal. Walsall was one of the centres which developed the necessary skills to produce these miniature works of art.

The first signs of the lower order of horsemen, the carters and waggoners, decorating the harness of their horses, was in the form of brass ovals and shields, as though imitating the family crests displayed on the blinkers and saddle pads of the elegant carriage horses.

A study of contemporary paintings shows evidence of these brass decorations in the early nineteenth century, but it is not until after 1850 that we find illustrations of the pendant type horse brasses. Certainly they are known to have existed earlier and there are many dated examples from the first half of the nineteenth century, but they were not in common enough use to attract attention of such artists as Stubbs, Pyne or the Herrings, all of whom produced detailed pictures of harnessed work-horses at this date.

Around 1850 horse brasses suddenly became fashionable, probably as a result of an unknown manufacturer in Walsall seizing the opportunity to satisfy the carters' desire to create a display of harness decorations as fine as that on carriage horses. Many of the early manufactured brasses have a form of 'crest' featured in their design. Walsall was already producing crests for the carriage harness and it was only a small step to produce similar ornaments in brass inside a hanging frame, for the waggoners to sport on their harness.

Hundreds of factories, from the largest down to the one person business, started to produce these horse brasses. Over 2,000 different designs are believed to exist, though some of the differences in the patterns are very slight – probably where manufacturers copied popular designs of their rivals.

Many of the larger manufacturers produced beautiful and elaborate catalogues of their products. One of the earliest of these was by the firm of Matthew Harvey of Bath Street, founded in 1838 and still going strong today. Their pattern room contains many of the original lead patterns shown in their catalogue of 1888. Another firm which has kept a large collection of their early patterns is Stanley Bros. of Long Street. This firm, founded in 1832, is the oldest in the town still producing harness fittings.

Among the patterns to be found, apart from purely geometric designs, are various trade motifs. For example, the miller's horses could be decorated with brasses incorporating wheatsheafs or windmills into their design; the farmer could choose from a variety of horse designs, and there were locomotive designs for railway carters. The brewers had a choice of barrel patterns and there were even crossed saws and tree motifs for the horses of timber merchants.

Commemorative brasses were also produced to celebrate special occasions, particularly those connected with royalty. Queen Victoria's Golden and Diamond Jubilees produced a wonderful crop of special brasses. Each subsequent royal occasion has produced its quota of designs. The Silver Jubilee of the Queen Elizabeth II saw the manufacture of at least twenty-five different designs of horse brass for the occasion – most of which were made in Walsall.

Apart from the pendant type horse brass, there were other forms of decoration produced to brighten the harness. These included the 'fly terret' – a miniature brass swinging in a ring mounted on a stem and often matching the design of a horse brass. It was usually worn on the top of the bridle – its original purpose being to keep the flies away from the horses' ears during hot weather.

Another form of decoration which started life with a real purpose was the bells. In their original form they were large bells mounted above the collar in sets of from two to five. Their ringing was loud enough to be heard at a distance which would act as a warning to oncoming waggon teams – especially in narrow lanes. Later bells are miniatures by comparison with the originals and made in various combinations principally for mounting on the saddle.

Hameplates were designed to decorate the top strap of the collar hames. Like the fly terret, they often matched a horse brass pattern.

The hames, fixed to the collar, provided the necessary attachments from which a horse could pull its load. Again, Walsall was the biggest centre for their manufacture and the firm of Walsall Hame and Cart Gear is the only one still producing cart horse hames in this country. For show purposes these hames are cased in sheet brass. Under the brass casting a steel covered wooden core provides the necessary strength. Walsall Hame and Cart Gear is also the last manufacturer of chain work for the heavy horse harness.

So we see that although the manufacture of harness furniture of the heavy horse died for almost thirty years, enough of the know-how and the patterns survived in Walsall to meet the needs of the renewed interest in the heavy horses over the past ten years and for many years to come.

TERRY KEEGAN, *HORSE BRASSES AND DECORATIONS*, 1990

Parades and their Awards

Having being engaged in researching horse parades recently, I was interested in the publicity given to current parades in the last issue of *Heavy Horse World* – particularly in the case of the Birmingham Parade, as Bryan Holden, largely responsible for the resurrection of this parade, is a member of the National Horse Brass Society who are sponsoring the brasses awarded.

Parades of one form or another have been held up and down the country for many years, village carnivals, May Day parades and harvest festivals being occasions for such parades, and horsemen were proud to display their animals and harness. In spite of this pride on show to the admiring public, it cannot be denied there was much cruelty involved in the working of horses, especially in the towns and cities. The founding of the RSPCA in 1826 was the beginning of a long, hard campaign to improve the lot of animals in general and of the horse in particular. Continual publicity, prosecutions and a growing public awareness of the situation led to a change in attitudes. One of the results of this campaigning was the introduction of horse parades in which the results of humane treatment were immediately obvious to all. A horse could not be ill treated for fifty-one weeks of the year and then shown at its best after one week's hasty preparation.

Parades, normally associated with draught horses, were of two types – public, or restricted to entries from a single organization such as a local council. Public parades were organized by a committee drawn from local

A line-up of Single Turnouts at the East of England Showground.

businessmen, equine societies, prominent philanthropists and organizations such as the RSPCA. Invariably, local dignitaries would give their support to help influence the prize fund. Entrants normally had to fulfil certain entry qualifications covering such matters as their normal area of work, age and use of harness and type of work. The majority of parades were divided into classes, with prizes in each. Examples of these classes included singles in waggons, pairs in waggons, singles in carts and classes for particular trades, such as brewers, coal merchants, builders and contractors etc.

Each class normally qualified for cash prizes in the range of £1 for first down to 2/6d (12½p) for fourth. Prizes in kind were also awarded, usually by local businessmen. For example, in the Plymouth Horse Parade of 1892 these included a tin of biscuits, a pair of trousers, a pair of boots, a box of Sunlight soap and an ornamented bridal cake. Many of the parades awarded a 'Merit Badge' or brass to the class winners, which was highly esteemed by the recipients.

Probably the best known of all parades, although not the oldest, are the two London Parades – The Cart Horse Parade and The Van Horse Parade. Unlike other parades, neither had classes, it being the intention of the organizing committees to set a standard by which every entrant would be judged on equal terms. Those qualifying received a cash reward and a red rosette.

The London Cart Horse Parade was first held in 1886 in Battersea Park, South London. Two years later it moved to its permanent home in Regents Park but it was not until 1895 that brass 'Merit Badges' were awarded by the RSPCA to all entrants receiving a red rosette. From a modest beginning of 138 horses parading in 1886, the figure was approaching the 1,000 mark in 1900, causing a strain on the organization. Suggestions were made that the large companies be restricted to two entries, or alternatively, a second prize for the lighter horses be introduced. The second idea was adopted and on Easter Monday, 1904, the inaugural parade of The London Van Horse Parade Society took place in Regents Park. RSPCA recognition of this parade was signified by the award of a Merit Badge in 1907. This was smaller than the brass awarded at the Cart Horse Parade and from 1907 onwards the same design was used for both parades, with the appropriate wording on each.

These two brasses continued to be awarded until 1935, when brass gave way to aluminium as the metal used. The last of these RSPCA shield shape Merit Badges was awarded in 1939 when the outbreak of war caused a suspension of the parades.

The parades restarted in 1946 with the Van Horse Parade Society introducing a horse-shoe shaped brass.

The number of entries in both parades gradually decreased until their successful futures were in doubt. To overcome this problem a meeting of the two Society committees decided on amalgamation under the title of the London Harness Horse Parade. The first parade took place on Easter Monday 1966 with the same horse shoe design brass being awarded but bearing the new title. A Centenary brass was produced in 1985 to mark the anniversary of the founding of the London Cart Horse Parade Society. This was rather clumsy and very disappointing.

Another parade brass acknowledging the involvement of the RSPCA is that awarded at the Norwich and District Horse Parade. The winners of each class received a brass of exceptional quality, being made by The Soho Metal and Scientific Instrument Works, in London. This firm was known for pattern and die making and also as medallists. This brass carries a very small version of the Royal Coat of Arms surrounded by the RSPCA motto: 'Be Merciful After Thy Power. Justice. Kindness.'

MALCOLM ANDREWS, *HEAVY HORSE WORLD*, 1987

ten

Vehicles, Crafts and Harness

The strongest horse is useless without something to pull, and the means to pull it. Craftsmen catering for these twin needs became a feature of the countryside. Without the carpenter, wheelwright, blacksmith and harness maker, the horseman could not operate. Here we look at the skills and devotion of a body of men who helped fashion the countryside as surely as those who owned or worked on it.

They knew every horse in the district, and their practical knowledge was augmented by helping with hay or harvest on summer evenings. Yet they never regarded themselves as craftsmen. They were people who worked long hours. They had been taught in no uncertain manner by older men to whom the craft had been handed down.

A Malton, North Yorkshire, saddler proudly displays his wares around 1900. These collars would be bought by Wolds farmers owning twenty or more working horses on their large arable farms. (John Stone)

Nor was there anything leisurely about their life. A carpenter had to make a wooden barrow or a cart naff (wheel centre) in a certain time, with no welfare considerations. One told me how tiring it was to work all day up to the knees in wood shavings, because no one had time to clear them.

The Harness of the Heavy Horse

The harness of a heavy horse used for draught work consists of three primary parts. There are (a) the collar, by which the horse pulls, (b) the pad, which takes the weight of shafts or pole, and (c) the bridle and strap-work. Basically, the harness is of leather, but the pad has a wooden frame, the collar is reinforced by wooden 'hames', to which are attached the chains by which the horse pulls its load, and there are other chains and metal joints at various strategic points.

Cart pads generally have a frame of elm wood, which rarely splits. They consist of two short, flat boards to fit on either side of the horse's spine and a curved, grooved 'bridge' attached to them at right-angles, over the spine. This frame is thoroughly padded on the underside with straw, felt or flock, the whole covered in a coarse flannel-like cloth on the under-side and shaped to fit the horse's back, and in leather on the upper-side.

The collar is a highly complex article, the making of which requires skilled craftsmanship. It consists of several parts, namely, the wale, the barge, the body and the facing. The wale, fundamentally, is a tube of leather stuffed with straw. The straw, ideally of unthreshed rye, must be packed in lengthwise, unbroken, in a kind of plaiting pattern, and the job is done while the leather is damp, so that the leather may shrink evenly around the packing.

The wale is shaped to the size of the horse's neck, and then sewn together, with a flap, known as the 'barge', left free along one side. To this 'barge' the body of the collar is sewn. The body is the padding of the collar, again consisting ideally of rye straw. Like the padding of the pad, it is covered with a very strong cloth, usually of woollen material, and known in the trade as 'body check', but sometimes of linen. Between the straw and the cloth a layer of fine wool flock is generally inserted. A rope is wedged between the wale and the barge, to strengthen the collar. Then the whole is covered with leather facing, sewn on while damp.

Although the basic pattern of collars is standard, within it there is infinite variety. Not only are there specialized types of collar for heavy horses, medium-heavies and lighter ones and for different kinds of work, but each horse has to be fitted individually. It is essential that the collar shall fit perfectly and that there shall be no awkward bumps or knots to gall the horse as it pulls.

664/
M 10/ The Exors of the Late W. Rawlington, Xmas 1924
another a/c

46, MARKET PLACE,

Dr. to **T. MENNELL,**

Saddle, Harness and Collar Maker,

DEALER IN ALL KINDS OF LEATHER GOODS.

POCKET FLASH LAMPS. ∴ MECCANO and PARTS IN STOCK.

Collars, Hames, Saddles, Breechings, Traces, Girths, and every
description of Light and Heavy Harness kept in stock.
REPAIRS OF EVERY DESCRIPTION DONE ON THE PREMISES.

A large stock of TRAVELLING REQUISITES always on hand.

Sole Agent for "LINDURA" Washable Waterproof Collars, Cuffs and Fronts,
like Linen in appearance.

5% Interest charged on Overdue Accounts. Accounts rendered Quarterly.

1924

Date	Description		£ s. d.
Feb 2.	2 Pair of Plough Cords @ 2/3 Pair		4. 6
25	Rep'd 1 headcollar with new leather &		3.-
Mar 6	Rep'a Horse neck Collar with 22 ys of new		
	leather & laces & new lining & stuffing		15-10
7	Rep' 4 Pair of Blinders, 1 Ploughing Bridle, 5 Trace		
	Backbands, 1 Trace Bellyband, 4 Plough		
	Backbands. 1 Cart Breeching, 3 headcollars		
	& 2 Pair of reins in various places with		
	leather & ironware. Material 43/10 Labour 34/9		3 18 7
18	Rep'a Cart saddle with 15 ys of new leather &		
	a new tree to covers & new lining & stuffing		1- 1- 8
April 1	To 1 Pair of Tan Sheepskin Button Leggins		15· 6
16	Rep' No 1 Horse neck Collar with leather & new		
	lining & stuffing		9· 9
	Rep' No 2 Ditto with leather & new lining & stuffing		12· 3
	Rep' 1 Pair of Cart Blinders with leather		
	S. hook Blinder ring &		4· 4
June 11	Rep' 2 Headcollars with new leather &		6· 1
July 5	2 Pair of Plough Cords @ 2/3		4. 6
Aug 25	6 stout Cart hameshaps @ 1/9 each		10· 6
30	2 Cart whips @ 3/10 each		7· 8
Sep 16.	Rep' 3 Pair of Cart Blinders with 14 ys of		
	new leather & buckles & rings & tirretts &		10· 1
Nov 18	Rep' 3 Headcollars with 1 lb 1 ys of new leather &		10· 10
Dec 1	1 Pair of Plough Cords		2· 3
13	1 Pair of Hedging Gloves		3· 6
15	1 Pair of Gloves for Grandson		2· 9
		£	11 · 6 · 10

This invoice shows the ancillary industries' place in the countryside. No farm could
function without the goods mentioned being in good repair.

176

Collar-making was such a skilled craft that in time it tended to become specialized. Basic collars, comprising wales, bridges and bodies, were made by experts in Bristol and other western towns, from whom saddlers in other parts bought them and fashioned them to suit their own clients. So specialized was the work that the saddler engaged on it preferred to twist and wax his own thread. Many saddlers, too, had rope-walks behind their shops, where they wound rope for reins (or 'cords', as they were commonly called).

Incidentally, for those who have never seen a cart-horse harnessed, the collar is put upside-down over the horse's head and twisted to its right position after it is resting on its neck.

The hames, usually of wood reinforced by iron but sometimes entirely of iron, were shaped to fit around the collar and were fastened by a leather strap at the top end and a chain at the bottom. To it were attached the trace chains on which the horse exerted its pull. The hames were, in fact, the essential part of the harness, the collar itself being the cushion which enabled the horse to draw such heavy loads without injury.

A chain, with close links fitted over the back and into the groove of the pad, took the weight of waggon or cart, so that none of the weight rested on the collar.

Along the back from the pad a broad leather strap rested on the horse's spine and connected with a crupper, which fitted around the base of the tail. From this strap other similarly broad straps hung down over the horse's flanks to connect with transverse pieces. To them short chains were attached, linking with the base of the vehicle shafts. It was these which enabled the horse to lean back in its harness to apply a brake or to back the vehicle.

The bridle was fashioned of straps of leather about an inch across and therefore wider than those of which the bridles of saddle and coach-horses were made. An almost inevitable feature of heavy horse bridles was the blinkers, which prevented the horse from seeing what was happening on either side or in the rear. I could never appreciate the need for these, for it seemed to me that a properly trained horse would not worry itself over such matters. However, it was the custom, and probably it served to compensate for errors in breaking in the horse in the first place.

The collar and bridle were essential parts of the harness no matter what work the horse was doing; the pad was used only when the horse was pulling a vehicle of some weight, such as a cart or a waggon. For lighter implements, the pad and associated straps were taken off and longer trace-chains were fixed from the implement to the hooks on the hames.

RALPH WHITLOCK, GENTLE GIANTS, 1976

Harnessing and Yoking

In its simplest form harnessing consists of attaching the horse's collar to an implement drawn along the ground, such as a horse hoe. One end of each trace chain is hung onto the hame hook, and the other end onto the swingletree or whippletree. These are made of wood, usually oak or ash, but iron is also used. Though iron swingletrees do not break easily, they can damage a kicking horse who, if he splinters a wooden bar, does no damage to himself. Some of those sedate horses on the Bayeux Tapestry were yoked to swingletrees.

If the load is too much for a shaft horse in cart or waggon, a trace horse is attached, sometimes only at the foot of an incline. Instead of the swingletree, the centre of which is hooked to the implement in a one-horse draught, a stretcher is used. This is a strong but light rod of wood, with a few links either side to take the trace horse's chains, and traces which hang in special eyes on the underside of the shafts. Trace horses must be watched. Some have a knack of keeping the chains tight and giving a semblance of pulling while the shaft horse is doing all the work!

When two horses are yoked side by side, a cobbletree, maisletree or baulk is generally needed, unless the implement or waggon takes the swingletrees direct.

John Peacock driving his favourite Unicorn hitch of Shires to the Ind Coope dray. (East of England Showground)

The cobbletree's purpose is to equalize the draft, so that its swingletrees are always attached to it at either end, but it has an adjustable crab hook in case one horse is assisted by a trace horse. This method of yoking is called bodkin fashion; to equalize the draught the crab hook is placed one third of the way along, instead of in the centre as when only two horses are yoked.

In the single-furrow, two-horse plough, one horse walks in the furrow – the furrow horse – and the other on the unploughed part – the land horse. Generally, each keeps to its own job, though some horses will take either role. A furrow horse does not require many brains; all it needs to do is set one foot in front of the others at its best pace, and follow the track so conveniently marked. More is required of a land horse which must keep a sensible distance from its partner, neither tugging wide nor boring.

In-line yoking was more common in the south of England. Three or even four horses walked one in front of the other in the furrow, obviating paddling the unploughed land in wet conditions. The *Standard Cyclopedia of Modern Agriculture* calls this the most wasteful method of yoking, but not uncommon on heavy land. The rear horse is known as the phill horse, the second the body horse, the next as the middle, and the front the fore horse or leader.

Three-horse yoking uses an adaptation of the swingletrees and cobbletree used for a pair. The crab hook is attached to the implement one third of the way along the cobbletree or evener, and an extra cobbletree is used. The principle was extended when yoking four horses in Britain, but four abreast make a clumsy team. Horses bunch and roll onto each other; they have no freedom of movement or circulating cool air. With so many skilled horsemen available cheaply, there was no pressure in Britain's inter-war period to devise newer methods, and four-horse yokes were rare.

EDWARD HART, *GOLDEN GUINEA BOOK OF HEAVY HORSES
PAST AND PRESENT*, 1976

Bridles

Open v Closed Bridles
The main function of a bridle is to hold a bit in the horse's mouth, to which can be attached reins for the person controlling the horse to communicate to it which way he wants it to move. For the majority of heavy horse bridles there is also a second function; to provide a means of restricting the sight of the horse, usually to a narrow, forward and downward field of vision. It is this secondary function that gives us our main division in the patterns of heavy horse bridles used in Great Britain – open bridles without blinkers and closed bridles with them.

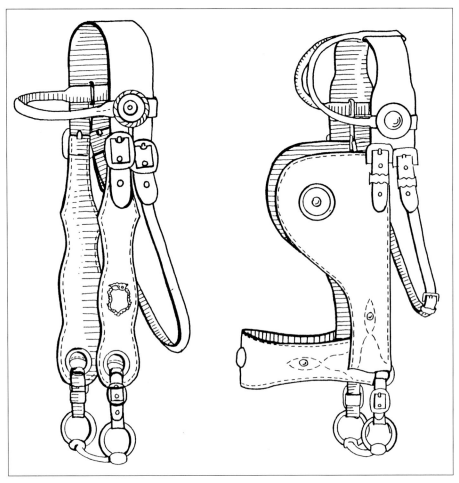

A Scottish open bridle (left) and a Scottish closed bridle (right).

Judges at shows seemed to prefer to see harnessed horses wearing blinkers. Certainly in Scotland, competitors showing heavy horses in harness believe they would stand a poor chance of a prize if they brought a horse into the ring wearing an open bridle. Many people genuinely believed that the addition of blinkers to the bridle added to the smartness of the whole harness. The smarter the turnout required and the more expensive the harness, the more likely the bridle was to be blinkered.

The harness-makers too opposed any change towards simplicity. Many believed that by reducing the price of a bridle by the cost of the blinkers, they would reduce their meagre margins to unacceptable levels. It is interesting to note that during the height of the campaign to do away with blinkers, the

Saddler's Trade Journal included in its pages a circular from one of the societies appealing to the trade to advocate their abolition to their customers. This was backed up by an editorial on the same subject and yet, for the next few months the journal ran articles on patterns of harness, all of which included blinkers on the bridles!

Open Bridle Patterns

Considering the fact that most young horses were trained to harness in some form of blinkerless bridle, it does seem strange that the use of the open bridle remained so limited, especially on the farms.

Even in parts of Scotland, where the open bridle was most commonly seen, young horses would often be trained in open bridles – 'an open yin lets them see roond aboot them', and later they would be converted to closed bridles 'tae stop them seeing ower much'.

But for the horsemen further north, living in bothies on farms working up to fifteen pairs of horses, to have to use 'blinders' on a horse was tantamount to not having the ability to handle them as any true horseman should. This north-eastern corner of Scotland was the stronghold of the open bridle where the men worked with the horses all day long cultivating the rich soil.

Further south in Fife and the Scottish Midlands, blinkers were preferred, but in southern Scotland the open bridle was again to be seen, especially around Lanarkshire and Peebles-shire, where at one time '90 per cent of the farmers in the district ploughed with horses wearing headstalls'. (A bit was attached to the headstall or manger-halter to turn it into a simple open bridle.)

One Glasgow harness-maker, as long ago as 1847, designed a set of harness which had removable blinkers. They were attached top and bottom by springs 'thus having a collar open or bridle closed as required'. The idea does not seem to have caught on.

The Full-faced Bridle

This early pattern of blinkered bridle survives in only a few districts of England and Wales, chiefly in southern Cornwall and the Hereford, Radnor borders. At one time it was more widely distributed in the southern part of Britain and is probably a survivor of the earliest form of blinkered bridle. There are examples of the pattern from the early eighteenth century in the Museum of Leathercraft at both Walsall and the Guildhall Museum in London.

The essential feature of the full-faced bridle is a broad piece of leather joining the top of the head-strap to the brow-band, and continuing down the front of the face to the nose-band. This gives a hooded effect on the horse wearing it, particularly as the nose-band tends to be thicker than normal. In its simplest form it is found with all but the head-strap cut out of one piece of very thick leather. Bridles of this pattern were made around Kington in Herefordshire until the last harness-maker closed shop. But they were not always liked by the wagoners. Bert Boulton, who has been with horses since he was ten, called them 'the owld fashioned bridles' and found them too heavy, as they tended to 'sweat a horse'. 'They were all right on a cold day.'

Around Penzance, where the pattern was being made by local saddler, Mr Nicholls, until recently, the same argument was used against it by local farmers. It was too hot for the horse in summer. In southern Cornwall these bridles are used as a show bridle, the majority of farmers being content with a cheaper bridle without the full-face piece.

TERRY KEEGAN, *THE HEAVY HORSE: ITS HARNESS AND HARNESS DECORATIONS*, 1973

The Smithy

The smith took the first shoe from the fire with his tongs, tapped it on the anvil to remove scale, laid it on edge and with carefully timed blows from the wedge-end of his four-sided Catshead hammer, hammered out a thin leaf-shaped skin of iron for the clip. He reheated the shoe, impaled it lightly with a punch,

Shoeing in the forge.

placed it near at hand on the floor. With the mare's ponderous front leg held easily between his knees, checking the fit by the toe-clip, he applied the burning iron to the pared hoof, lightly to begin with and then intermittently with on and off pressure until the horn began to sizzle and throw out green pungent clouds like some Luciferan snuff. Each hoof was burned, and final shoe titivations made on the anvil before they were ready to nail.

Nailing on horse shoes, his big calloused hands acquired an eloquent sensitivity. The shoeing smith – the only craftsman to do so – has to work with living material, the horn which receives the nails is small, the quick near. Never any gossiping or straying attention now. With the shoe held in position with fingers and palm, Meiriog placed the first of the seven, slightly curving, soft-metalled horseshoe nails into the second hole from the heel. He began to hammer, feeling and exploring with his fingers for the emerging point and then hammering home the nail head as far as it would go, bending the end before twisting it off with the claw of the small shoeing hammer.

The day's first shoeing was over by eight o'clock. There was already another horse waiting outside. The smith straightened his back, and David Evans the carter slowly backed his huge placid mare into the daylight for the journey home.

LLEWELYN JONES, *SCHOOLIN'S LOG*, 1980

Making Models of Horse-drawn Vehicles

In this, the space age, it is sometimes difficult to imagine that not so many years ago the major form of transport was the horse-drawn vehicle, and it is surprising how many tens of thousands there must have been in this country alone.

Although we consider today's achievements as outstanding, the horse-drawn vehicles of yesteryear could also claim similar distinctions, for each type was built for a specific purpose. The styles varied from light delivery carts and wagons to the large drays for hauling all types of heavy load, together with various light and heavy farm carts and wagons.

Horse power obviously varied with the conditions, with the lighter trades vehicles using one or two light horses such as the cob, while the heavier vehicles usually had two, four, six or even more of a heavy breed. Farm carts or wagons usually had one or two heavies.

Because of the many types and variations in design, horse-drawn vehicles are fascinating subjects for modelling in themselves. In the nomenclature alone, one will soon discover a vocabulary strange to the modern ear, but full of memories to the older generation.

The hobby of making model horse-drawn vehicles is perhaps the least publicised of all, but it is rapidly gaining a large following in all age groups.

Unlike a few years ago, when anyone wanting to make a model had virtually to go out and find a suitable vehicle and painstakingly take all measurements, draw up his own sketches, or perhaps work off old photographs, the modellers of today have at their disposal a large and fine selection of drawings for virtually any horse-drawn vehicle. Emphasis appears to be on farm carts and wagons, with stage-coaches and the carriage fairly well represented. Perhaps the light tradesman's vans are the least known.

Although these drawings offer good value in their own rights, they do vary considerably in presentation. Many are based on careful measurement and study of actual vehicles, give details to exact scale and include comprehensive instruction charts and advise on tools, materials and methods. Others are simply scale drawings only, and do not give any measurements. They come in ⅛, ¹⁄₁₀ or ¹⁄₁₂ scale.

To avoid disappointment, there are several golden rules that should be observed. Before deciding on what type of model to build, first consider where it will be placed. All too often one makes a beautiful model only to find that the place it was intended for is unsuitable, and, although it may not at first be the intention to have one of the many types of pottery horse in the shafts, sooner or later this will be the case.

Little in the way of hand tools is required, unless, of course, you want to make your own wheels, when a small lathe is needed. It is however, possible to purchase ready-made wooden wheels either completed or in kit-form. Although the dedicated modeller abhors them, there are various sizes of plastic, wood-grain-finish wheel available. These are very realistic, and for the novice can be a big help, as the wheel must surely present the most difficult part to make of any model. Beware though: make sure the correct-size wheel is obtained. Materials can be purchased at many DIY shops, although much can be found about one's own workshop.

By far the simplest model to start with is the Welsh truckle cart, and, although this is not in any way a fancy one, it is nevertheless nice looking. The wheels are simply cut out of solid timber, allowing more concentration on the bodywork.

Next came the tipping or non-tipping carts, and here we have a very wide choice with far too many to go into much detail. The most common model is the farm tip cart. Basically a cart body is a box on wheels, hinged on the axle and having the simplest of tipping devices, either the upright tipping stick at front of cart, the slope of tip being controlled by bolts placed through holes in the stick, or by the provision of a removable tip rod positioned across the shafts close to the body. The former must surely have been the better and safer of the two.

Mainly root crops were carried, but stones and materials for general farm work were sometimes transported, and at harvest times the carts could easily be converted by fitting harvest ladders on to the front and back on the top.

Second choice is the dung cart which, due to its dense loads, was much more robustly built. The side and front boards always sloped outward from the bottom, and the floorboards mainly ran lengthways to the body to allow the loads to slide out more easily when tipped.

After mastering these types, the modeller usually next turns to the wagon. Here we have three basic types: the box wagon, the hoop raved wagon, and the barge or boat wagon. The range in these is very extensive, as almost every county had its own design, although some did not.

In the box wagon range, the most popular choice must surely be the Hereford, either the plank-sided type or the panel-sided one, with the latter being the more detailed and pleasant looking. The plank-sided type later superseded the panel-sided as it was much easier and cheaper to mass produce. Next in popularity as far as modelling goes must be the East Anglian wagon, and although this type is rather big and square it is nevertheless a nice-looking wagon, with much of its woodwork chamfered. Due to its size, it carried a heavy load and was usually fitted with twin shafts, unlike most others which usually had single shafts.

In the hoop raved wagon, the Somerset and Oxfordshire wagons make good projects. They are similarly constructed to box wagons, except that they have raised curved sides extending over the rear wheels.

Perhaps the barge and boat wagons are the least modelled, but they are just as interesting as any of the others. As their names indicate, these wagons tend to look like boats built on wheels.

As with the cart, the build up of the wagon floor varied; some were cross-boarded and others were long-boarded. There was apparently no hard or fast rule about this, especially as wagons used solely for harvest work did not need longboards. If stones etc were to be carted, then this method was obviously best.

The forecarriages of wagons varied immensely from county to county, as did the body side supports; some of the latter were beautifully chamfered in timber while others were in iron work.

With few exceptions, all carts and wagons were painted. Red was predominant for wheels and undercarriages, and either blue, yellow or brown for bodywork, again depended on locality.

It is no exaggeration to say that from start to finish perhaps 150 hours or even more will be spent on building up any wagon model, but at the end it will be something to be proud of. It is often said that no doubt the full sized wagons were turned out in less time than the models.

As well as making carts and wagons, the heavy horse modeller will make ploughs and other farm implements, and these can be just as interesting.

J.B. PEARCE, *HEAVY HORSE & DRIVING*, 1977

The Old-time Forge

The old-time forge would usually be sited in the centre of the village it served, quite often near a crossroads. A fairly large forecourt was useful for the waiting horses and vehicles, with a drinking trough and with loops on the walls for tethering the animals. Somewhere outside there would be an iron wheelplate, about six feet in diameter, embedded in the ground for use when a wooden wheel was to be shod with its iron tyre. The chestnut tree, poetically symbolic of the village smithy, would be grown for the shade it cast on hot sunny days.

Inside, the hearth and fire form the forge proper, although now the word 'forge' usually refers to the whole of the smith's working premises. The fire is on a raised hearth, usually of bricks, with a canopy and chimney over it. Some places might have a double hearth, with the bellows system between, serving either hearth as required. The bellows create the draught of air needed to bring the fire to sufficient temperature to heat the iron for working. A lever with a cowhorn handle was used to hand-operate the bellows. (Today an electrically driven blower is often used.) A blast pipe or tuyere projects directly into the fire. It is connected to the bellows by a pipe and is often water-cooled, the water being contained in an open-topped tank behind the hearth. Water is also kept in the cooling trough at the front of the hearth. This is used for cooling tools and for quenching certain work.

JOCELYN BAILEY, *THE VILLAGE BLACKSMITH*, 1977

Wheel-stuff

In the same winter weeks, while the wheelwright's trade was quiet and the master was superintending the sawyers and helping the less skilled men stack the boards and planks out-o'-doors for seasoning – in those same weeks, within doors, the older and trustier men, who needed no supervision, were busy with the new spokes and felloes. (In this word leave out the o. Make the word rhyme to bellies.) Well experienced in all wheels, and understanding what was sure to be wanted for waggon or cart in years to come, these men required no telling what to do. They knew well enough. All the wheel-making lore of the country-side for generations guided their judgment.

The felloe-blocks from the saw-pit required roughly shaping while still green, before they too could be stacked up for seasoning; for although hard enough in all conscience they would be far harder years hence, when the sap had dried out of them and they came to be used. Now was the time. And much remained to be done to them. The sawyers had but halved the smaller blocks, putting a longitudinal cut down the middle, so that now there were two pieces, each piece half cylindrical. It was the wheelwright's business to chop each of these pieces into a felloe, as large and long as the timber would make. Or if, as sometimes happened, there had been material enough in either half to make two felloes, still the sawyers (following a line pencilled for them by the master out in the yard) had but cut this one curved line. It was left to the men in the shop to trim the felloes down sideways and to shape out the rounded back to the outer piece, the hollow belly to the inner.

The tools were axe and adze and sometimes hand-saw, and the implements (besides a square) a chopping block and a felloe-horse. Yet it is in vain to go into details at this point; for when the simple apparatus had all been got together for one simple-looking process, a never-ending series of variations was introduced by the material. What though two felloes might seem much alike when finished? It was the wheelwright himself who had to make them so. He it was who hewed out that resemblance from quite dissimilar blocks, for no two felloe-blocks were ever alike. Knots here, shakes there, rind-galls, waney edges (edges with more or less of the bark in them), thicknesses, thinnesses, were for ever affording new chances or forbidding previous solutions, whereby a fresh problem confronted the workman's ingenuity every few minutes. He had no band-saw (as now) to drive, with ruthless unintelligence, through every resistance. The timber was far from being a prey, a helpless victim, to a machine. Rather it would lend its own subtle virtues to the man who knew how to humour it: with him, as with an understanding friend, it would co-operate. So, twisting it, turning it 'end for end,' trying it for an inch or two this way and then an inch or two that, a skilful wheel-maker was able to get the best possible product from his timber every time. I don't think I ever afterwards, in the days of band-saws, handled such a large proportion of superlatively good felloes as used to pass through my hands in those days of the axe and adze. Perhaps the sawn-out felloes look better – to a theorist from an office. But at the bench you learn where a hard knot may be even helpful and a wind-shake a source of strength in a felloe; and this was the sort of knowledge that guided the old-fashioned wheelwright's chopping.

GEORGE STURT, *THE WHEELWRIGHT'S SHOP*, 1923

The Process of Hooping

From the wheelwright's shop the wheel is taken to the blacksmith for tiring. In most country districts the wheelwright's shop and the blacksmith's forge are located in the same place, and most wheelwrights are competent to work both in wool and in metal. In the small hamlet of Sarnau, Cardiganshire, for example, the wheelwright and blacksmith lived next door to one another until 1956. For the tiring process at least two men are required for the work.

Cutting

First of all a bar of metal, some sixteen feet long, two-and-a-half inches wide and three-quarters of an inch thick is laid flat on the ground. A chalk mark is made on the rim of the measuring-wheel or *traveller*, a wheel about ten inches across with a handle attached to its axle, and another mark is made on the rim of the untired wheel. With the chalk marks as starting-points the traveller is pushed around the wheel rim and the number of turns noted. It is then run along the bar of iron in order to obtain the correct length of iron required for the tire. Allowance has to be made however for 'shutting' or welding the loose ends of the tire, and for the expansion of the tire when heated. Generally for a wheel five feet in diameter, the diameter of the tire should be approximately one five-eighths of an inch less than the wheel. As soon as the correct length is ascertained the bar is cut off to the chalk mark. One man holds a cold chisel over the iron as it rests on the anvil, while another strikes it with a sledge-hammer.

The next operation is known as 'scarfing down', and it consists of flattening each end of the bar with a sledge-hammer. Each end is heated, hammered, and a hole punched through each scarf. The iron is then passed through the rollers of the tire-bender to the required shape. In the older country workshops, the tire was bent by hand on a post-bender, a difficult and intricate process.

Shutting

The next stage is the 'shutting' or welding of the two loose ends of the tire to form a complete hoop. By straining the two ends together, a nail is thrust through the holes that have been punched in the scarfs, and the joint welded. After welding, two or three nail-holes are punched in the tire; all is now ready for the process of tiring the wheel.

Tiring

An open fire of wood shavings, straw or peat is made in the corner of the yard and the tire placed on them. In some wheelwright's yards, a special type of upright brick oven, the furnace, is used for heating the tire, and within this oven one or two tires can be heated at the same time. Meanwhile the untired wheel is screwed down on the tiring platform, which is a permanent feature in the wheelwright's yard. By means of a very heavy screwed rod fixed to a ring below the central hole of the heavy iron tiring-platform, the wheel is fixed face downwards. The rod passes through the hubs of the wheel, while the rim lies outspread on the surrounding platform. With the wheel fixed rigidly to the tiring platform, the nave resting in the central hole, and the spokes and felloes supported along their whole length by the face of the platform, all is now ready for the tiring process. Two or three men with long handled tiring-tongs, grasp the red-hot tire from the fire and throw it down on the ground, so that all pieces of fuel and rubbish adhering to it are knocked off. It is grabbed again and dropped into position on the wheel. It is levered with tire-dogs and beaten with sledge-hammers until it is in place. Water is then poured on the rim, and as the tire shrinks the wheel is tightened under the enormous pressure of contraction.

The amount of dish on a wheel can be controlled by adjusting the central screws of the tiring-platform. Since the wheel is placed on the platform face downwards, that is with the convexity towards the back, the effect of the tire is to pronounce the dish.

J. GERAINT JENKINS, *AGRICULTURAL TRANSPORT IN WALES*, 1962

eleven

Poets and Artists

Though many artists tended to paint only their patrons' blood horses, hunters and children's ponies, there was always a nucleus giving full play to their admiration of the heavy horse. For them we must be thankful on two counts. Living in a world dependent on horse power, they understood their subjects' muscle structure, action and strength. This they transferred to canvas, and their successors have continued to delight with vivid impressions.

An astonishing number of older farmers and farm workers have, with no formal art training, made magnificent sketches and paintings of the heavy horses of their younger days. Others have played positive roles in advising and correcting established artists on exact harness details; no wrong size or number of links in a shoulder chain is undetected, each hame strap buckle must be precisely correct. Geraldine Freeman, painter of Suffolks from Coles Green, Framlingham, Suffolk, praises her coterie of former horsemen who see that each collar, strap and chain on her gleaming chesnuts is as it should be.

Cold Harbour Farm

This is the reason why
my verse is couched
in ploughman's plodding metre.
The slow, the rhythmic,
easy rise and fall
of feet that walked
wide acres,
through the seasons
that I knew and made.
One amongst so many men,
that have no name,
no monument, no lettered page
inscribed.

Who by their sweat and
subtle skills,
brought summer to
the barren fields,
and played their part
in painting England's
pastoral.
In this small corner
of the Chiltern hills.

DAVID B. NIXON, *THE SONG OF THE CHILTERNS*, 1978

Why Do You Paint that Type of Horse?

I am often asked, 'Why do you not paint the horse in its utmost perfection – the thoroughbred horse?' I am not quite sure why myself, but surely it is not that perfection in its cultivated form is not paintable from the artist's point of view. The thoroughbred horse is known to move in a certain manner. Its form, appearance, action and everything about it are understood and tabulated. Now what is left in this case for the painter, who, poor thing, would like a little something left for him to do, but who must not deviate from this perfectly understood form by a single hair. But this *other Type* is always interesting – I mean, the Natural Type fashioned by nature and not by man – full of faults, variable, beautiful, and lovable beyond words.

DAVID MESSUM, *THE LIFE AND WORKS OF LUCY KEMP-WELCH*, 1976

Sacrament (1937)

(To the memory of Charlie Long who taught me to plough)

The sweating horses stand in welcome shade
of hazel hedgerow flanking wood-field glade.
The ploughman's timepiece points the hour of one
Some sparrows see the well-earned lunch begun
Who breaks the loaf and gulps the cooling drink
Performs a priestly office so I think,
As when the bread is broke the wine outpoured
Where mankind shares the supper of the Lord.

REVD PHILIP WRIGHT, *RUSTIC RHYMES*, 1985

191

The Auld Farmer's New-year Morning Salutation to his Auld Mare, Maggie

On giving her the accustomed ripp of corn to hansel in (greet) the New Year

A Guid New-Year I wish thee, Maggie!
Hae, there's a ripp to thy auld baggie: *(belly)*
Tho' thou's howe-backit, now, and knaggie. *(hollow-backed, bony)*
I've seen the day,
Thou could hae gaen like onie staggie
Out-owre the lay.
Tho' now thou's dowie, stiff, an' crazy,   *(drooping)*
An' thy auld hide as white's a daisie.
I've seen thee dappl't, sleek and glaizie.   *(glossy)*
A bonie gray:
He should been tight that daur't to raize thee   *(alert)*
Ance in a day.

ROBERT BURNS

An evocative snowstorm picture attributed to Ben Herring. All weathers come alike to horses determinedly pulling along the rough track. (Sally Mitchell Prints)

Septembers Husbandrie

Horse, Oxen, plough, tumbrel, cart, waggon, & waine,
    the lighter and stronger, the greater thy gaine.
The soile and the seede, with the sheafe and the purse,
    the lighter in substance, for profite the wurse.
THOMAS TUSSER, *FIVE HUNDRED POINTS OF GOOD HUSBANDRY*, (1524?–80)

A Digression to Husbandlie Furniture

Barne locked, gofe ladder, short pitchforke and long,
    flaile, strawforke and rake, with a fan that is strong:
Wing, cartnave and bushel, peck, strike readie hand,
    get casting sholve, broome, and a sack with a band.

A stable wel planked, with key and a lock,
    walles stronglie wel lyned, to beare off a knock:
A rack and a manger, good litter and haie,
    sweete chaffe and some provender everie daie.

A pitchfork, a doongfork, seeve, skep and a bin,
    a broome and a paile to put water therein:
A handbarow, wheelbarow, sholve and a spade,
    a currie combe, mainecombe, and whip for a Jade.

A buttrice and pincers, a hammer and naile,
    an aperne and siszers for head and for taile:
Hole bridle and saddle, whit lether and nall,
    with collers and harneis, for thiller and all.

A panel and wantey, packsaddle and ped,
    A line to fetch litter, and halters for hed.
With crotchis and pinnes, to hang trinkets theron,
    and stable fast chained, that nothing be gon.
                    THOMAS TUSSER (1524?–80)

As the Team's Head-Brass

As the team's head-brass flashed out on the turn
The lovers disappeared into the wood.
I sat among the boughs of the fallen elm
That strewed the angle of the fallow, and
Watched the plough narrowing a yellow square
Of charlock. Every time the horses turned
Instead of treading me down, the ploughman leaned
Upon the handles to say or ask a word,
About the weather, next about the war.
Scraping the share he faced towards the wood,
And screwed along the furrow till the brass flashed
Once more.
    The blizzard felled the elm whose crest
I sat in, by a woodpecker's round hole,
The ploughman said. 'When will they take it away?'
'When the war's over.' So the talk began—
One minute and an interval of ten,
A minute more and the same interval.
'Have you been out?' 'No.' 'And don't want to,
  perhaps?'
'If I could only come back again, I should.
I could spare an arm. I shouldn't want to lose
A leg. If I should lose my head, why, so,
I should want nothing more. . . . Have many gone
From here?' 'Yes.' 'Many lost?' 'Yes, a good few.
Only two teams work on the farm this year.
One of my mates is dead. The second day
In France they killed him. It was back in March,
The very night of the blizzard, too. Now if
He had stayed here we should have moved the tree.'
'And I should not have sat here. Everything
Would have been different. For it would have been
Another world.' 'Ay, and a better, though
If we could see all all might seem good.' Then
The lovers came out of the wood again:
The horses started and for the last time
I watched the clods crumble and topple over
After the ploughshare and the stumbling team.

EDWARD THOMAS, COLLECTED POEMS, 1928

Tribute Due

What can you know,
whose hands have
never held
plough handles?
Nor felt the lines
soft pull on
velvet mouths;
the urgent kissing
of the plough,
upon brown face
of earth.
Riding as ship
the billowed contours
of the world,
bidding the white gulls
dance, at the marriage of man
to earth.

Breasting the hill
with blaze of burnished brass
and proud plumes nodding.
Pivoting on headlands
their feet like iron
dinner plates,
as delicate as dancers.
How can you know
whose way has ever been
beyond the hedge?

Nor followed head in air
the ring roll,
as the lark sang high,
boots sinking soft
in a kindly tilth.
Broke head beneath
the blackthorn bright
with stars,
whilst Captain tossed
his bag of chaff
beside the hedge.

195

Then on again
long wheel mark walking,
looking far
beyond the teeming drill
to boundary fence,
scattering shoe-shine rooks
as we bowled along.

Remember that the bread
you eat this day,
was borne upon the
backs of horses,
in those seasons past.
Without them then
there was no harvest now,
they bore the burden
of the harvest wains,
those towering galleons
of gold.
Until upon some
unknown harvest field,
the last sheaves crowned
the final load
and patient and enduring
still,
the horses drew away.
Leaving the stubble bare
beneath the moon.
Leaving an unknown
waggoner
to shut the gate.

DAVID B. NIXON, 1978

Bronze Champions on Display

Thanks to a recent gift, the Victoria and Albert Museum has acquired a note of rusticity. The gift is 18 animal bronzes by the American sculptor Herbert Haseltine, who died at the age of 85 in 1962, presented by the sister of the late George Davey, whom many will no doubt remember when he managed the firm of Knoedler in London, and who was in command there in 1930 when

Bronze of the Shire stallion Field-Marshal V, by Herbert Haseltine. The stallion was champion at the Royal Show in 1920 and 1921.

these animals were first exhibited. The point about them is that they are not ordinary animals but, apart from one or two of the horses, are all portraits either of prizewinners at important shows of the 1920s or exceptional in some other way.

The series now to be seen at the museum begins with the shire stallion, Field-Marshal V, belonging to King George V, who was champion at the Royal Show in 1920 and 1921. Haseltine spent several weeks at Sandringham modelling him; that gave him the idea of modelling other cart-horse breeds, and afterwards it was an obvious development to make bronzes of cattle, sheep and pigs. These original models were all quite small, but he made larger versions of the more popular ones, notably the horses at a guess about three times the size.

The larger version of the shire horse, for instance is 12 in. high from the tip of his ears to his feathered feet, that of a Suffolk Punch perhaps half an inch less. This last animal, champion in 1921 and 1922, was Sudbourne Premier, bred and owned by Lord Manton and later purchased by Mrs P.C. Vestey.

His stable was too dark to work in and it was too cold for him to stand still for any length of time (the month was December) so Haseltine had him walked round and round in a wide circle. For some reason, wrote the sculptor later, he became a favourite model with museums: one bronze was bought by the French Government, and others by the Tate Gallery, the Field Museum, Chicago, the San Francisco Museum and the Philadelphia Museum, and he gave one to Eton, where his son was then at school.

FRANK DAVIS, *COUNTRY LIFE*, DECEMBER 1970

Cart Horses

Horses are quite different in temperament [from cattle], and if I wanted to draw them I used to tether them in the yard, put a net of hay in front of their noses, and they would be good for hours, or as long as the hay lasted. I also followed them about as they grazed in the pasture and made quick notes of their movements, the only drawback to this being that the horses were always inclined to graze away from me and so present a three-quarter back view most of the time.

[The drawing on this page] was made while the horses were seeking relief from the hot sun, in the shade of a tree. They had grazed well and were inclined to sleep, and moved only to swish their tails or to kick forward with a hind foot at the flies which continually pestered them.

Pigs are very good to draw. They have interesting form and, providing they are not too fat, are quite beautiful. But they should be approached carefully, for if they are surprised they do not settle again easily. Often have I crept cautiously to the door of the sty and, on seeing the pigs asleep, have started to draw them. Then, perhaps, I have made a slight noise. One pig immediately opens it pale blue eyes and, on seeing my head above the door, gives a startled bark and jumps up; the others, without waiting to find the cause of the disturbance, do likewise and rush away, probably into the darkest recesses of the sty. Make no mistake, pigs are most intelligent animals!

C.F. TUNNICLIFFE, *MY COUNTRY BOOK*, 1942

Prince

A hook breaks: just a hook of the plough trace, that connects it to the pulling tree of the plough, and I take the length of chain to the blacksmith to have a new hook welded on. He is sitting on his anvil talking to a friend, while his mate hammers shoes he had just forged upon the hooves of a van-horse.

That hook was on Prince's plough-trace: it hitched him to the first load he pulled, gave him his first taste of work. That was not a plough, but a log of wood; to be precise, an old railway sleeper. The iron horse and the horse of flesh and blood have fortuitous inter-connections.

Horses have a language between themselves that a man may understand. When my old mare Kitty came home tired from the plough or the dung-cart, Prince would bound to meet her at the horse-yard gate. He would escort her to the stable, snapping playfully at her neck. 'What have you been up to all this time, to get you in that sweat?' 'Work.' 'What's work? You're always talking about work.' 'You wait, you'll see,' said Kitty.

Time passed, and Prince laughed at the idea of work. The old horsekeeper did not seem to have any intention of making Prince work. Every morning the harness would be put on Kitty, and her tucked-up and rather drooping body expressed a deep sigh: 'Why always me? Look at that fat, hefty young thing at your side.' Prince pranced after her through the yard. 'If you don't like it, why put up with it?' And Kitty put her ears back, showing the whites of her eyes. 'You wait.'

It seemed as though Prince might wait, and mock, for ever. Kitty had become a habit with the old horsekeeper, like the cobwebs on the ceiling that were never swept down, and the broken forks and the worn-out horse-collars, that were useless but never thrown away.

But one day another and a younger man followed the old horsekeeper into the stable. The horses were aware of a new presence in the gloom cast by the smoky old lantern. He listened to the old horsekeeper telling his old stories, but when there came a pause he spoke of things that must be done today and tomorrow.

'Tomorrow we'll start to break him in.' Old Jim had nothing more to say, but looked funereal.

'Mr Prince, now you look out,' cried puss, and darted off after a mouse as old Jim and I entered the stable.

'What's this they've put in my mouth. I can bite it, but I can't swallow it. I don't like this thing round my neck, and all this jingling-jangling whenever I move.'

'You'll get used to it.' chuckled Kitty.

A bridle and harness look strange on a colt at first. The blinkers seem to quench his natural fire. 'Now, at last,' I said to myself, as we led Prince out. I had waited months for this day, though it was to be anything but a holiday. It was July now, and I had planned to break him in in April. First it had been the state of the ground, then it had been his bad foot, now old Jim was objecting it was the wrong time of the year – too hot, too many flies – hoping perhaps to lead round to the spring again, and 'ground too hard.' But I was determined on it, however torrid, however many flies. This horse should cheat me and the farm no longer. Jim, as he brought Boxer's old collar to put upon Prince, reminded me of an undertaker's mute handing a wreath. He looked so lugubrious I almost had to laugh, until I reflected that this man was a horsekeeper, a ploughman by profession from his youth up, by choice and by heredity. Yet I must break *him* in to the idea of taming this colt.

So we took him upon the fallow field: the soil was deep and loamy, because I had harrowed it after a shower, breaking down the clods – too soon for the good of the fallow, but for the sake of breaking the colt. Prince sank his hooves in it; he plunged and began to run (as he thought) away. His surprise at being pulled up sharp by that thing in his mouth was complete. Jim and I had each a firm hold of an end of new plough-line; sometimes Prince veered towards me, and Jim pulled him up; sometimes towards Jim, and I did. Sometimes it was as much as both of us could do to hold him: we had to run, and crouch, and run again.

Soon Prince was covered with a white lather, as though he had been dipped in the wash-tub. The sweat ran down our faces, and I could feel it trickling down my chest and back.

Prince reared up, became heraldic, rampant, puissant. He was the great war-horse of old England. He tried to jump out of the harness of toil back into the age of tilt-yard and spear and panoply. His hooves were hammers of death to any that might be under; but muffled by the deep fallow they fell silently. It looked like Prince's country dance.

Prince, too, in a while had done. He reared no more; he leaped no more, nor ran, nor walked, but stood nonplussed. His flanks heaved; he had run himself to a standstill. He stood bewildered. The first stage was over.

We let him stand like that for awhile, then chirruped at him to proceed. He moved only his ears. We twitched the reins and prodded him. In a minute he started to go forward at a quiet, measured pace. It was his first movement in obedience to human command.

Presently we unhooked the plough-traces from where they were looped up to the hames, and hooked them to a whippletree attached by a chain to an old railway sleeper. This was the second stage in his education.

He felt for the first time the load against his shoulders when he pulled. He started backwards, sideways, and found himself caught in the chains. Then followed a to-do, out of which he tried to jump again; but he did not leap far with a railway sleeper for partner. Once more he started forward quietly, dragging the sleeper, until the noise the sleeper made scraping over the earth frightened him, and he tried to run away from it. We hung on until the cord bit into our flesh, and presently he realized that the noise was with him all the time, like the weight against his shoulders.

Old Jim was in his element. Strangely, after the first delay and difficulty of bringing him to the point of leading out Prince upon Spring Field, he was now all for making a thorough job of it. His small stature confronted the great horse with the assurance of a toreador: he allowed Prince to wind himself up in the chains by making him turn sharply, crying out, 'There, that's just what I wanted you to do: now you know what plough-traces feel like.' And Prince would stagger and try to kick, and almost sit down. Then we disentangled him, old Jim venturing daringly near his hind feet to do so, with only a 'Woa' for protection. I marvelled at this man, for months evading, deferring the day; preferring for work-mate the slow, meek Kitty. Now he was thoroughly roused out of himself, and wild horses were his pleasure.

Three Old Pals, by Malcolm Coward. Horses that have worked long together develop a fine understanding. (Sally Mitchell Prints)

'Give me that other rein. Now, gee up, Prince.' Leaping upon the log, he drove the horse himself: he stood balanced upon the swaying, lurching thing, speeding over the fallow. It became a sport, something between surf-riding and sledging, being dragged on that narrow craft over the brown waves of earth, the kind of feat for which natives of fine physique are admired. This little old toil-worn figure could balance perfectly.

We led Prince back to the stable, blown and drooping. Kitty trotted across the yard to meet him, and made a playful bite at his neck. Prince did not respond. He ate his oats and chaff, and continued with his head low in the manger. Kitty cocked her ears to and fro, a high-headed, holiday Kitty. 'Now, my lad, you know.'

The next day, after more of the log, we hitched him to the plough beside Kitty. This was a real pull, and Kitty let him feel it, not over-exerting herself. 'You've asked often enough what work is, now you've the chance to find out.' Prince was all of a fluster: once or twice he reared himself into a war-horse again. But we made him lean into the collar and pull. Every time the plough was turned at the end of the furrow, he of course became entangled in the chains. He was impatient to stand, yet unwilling to go: the furrows of that ploughing were a graph of Prince's behaviour, which was erratic. Kitty became his tutor. 'Now then, clumsy, don't come barging up against me: I'm supposed to be walking in this furrow.' First he would push her out over the ploughed land, then pull her on to the unploughed. Prince, I think, received a lecture on ploughing manners that night in the stable.

'What a state you're in: anybody would think you'd ploughed an acre. I wish Boxer were here to see you.'

'Boxer's pulling a dust-cart round the town,' said the stable cat. 'I've seen him. Children give him apples. Good stable; pleasant company; lots of corn and short hours: very happy. He says, "Next time hooves are polished don't be sad." '

'Now,' I said, 'we'll put Prince between a pair of shafts.'

'It would be best to start him off between the shafts of the roller.'

We led him out, more 'clothed' than ever before, looking like a wild tribesman who has put on hat and coat. I can never suppress a feeling of shame (hardly too strong a word for it) in cluttering for the first time the clean lines of a horse with bridle, bit, blinkers and harness. Prince had grown to take the freedom of the farm as his by right. But I knew the hour had come: either now he would rule us or we should rule him.

To put a horse into a cart for the first time is rather like experimenting with the atomic bomb – you never know when it, or he, is going off; or, in fact, what is going to happen. You do know that the descent of shafts on either side of him is going to be a shock, likewise the rumble of wheels behind him. Our method was to make Kitty draw the cart to the manure heap in the field, then lead Prince out to it.

The shafts came down over his shoulders: it is always a nice matter whether he swings his haunches aside before the shafts have caught and trapped them. Rather like the chip-chop part of Oranges and Lemons. Then to keep him still while a good heavy load of manure was loaded upon the cart. All worked at high pressure to achieve this, and by the time Prince's restlessness was becoming unmanageable he had three-quarters of a ton to drag along with him over soft earth.

Away he went, with Jim and I on either side, each holding a rein. He plunged over the ground, snorting and fuming; a wondrous engine of power. Once more he tried to jump, run, plunge into freedom.

I prayed for the steady nerve and mind of men who had gone before and achieved the mastery. Old Jim had been visited again by their spirit. The change in this man, when the encounter with horse was on, was another miracle. It expressed itself in continuous monologue to the horse. He and Prince were engaged in deep debate of mind and muscle, locked in a grip of such tense persuasion as wrings a supple withy to make a bond.

Prince soon had enough of pulling the cart as though it were a fire-engine, and dropped into a walk. From a walk into a stand. When he stood the thing behind him was silent, and the pressure on his collar was eased. So he thought the best way to forget it was to stand still in it. But we thought otherwise. The next time he moved forward it was at our command. The rest of the day he spent in carting manure. For the loading of the last load, he stood at the heap with no one at his head.

'Oh, he's *all right*,' cried Jim confidently. 'All he wants is use.'

'We'll use him every day for everything,' I decreed, and we parted for the night in that frame: the sunset sky glowed with our achievement.

I slumped down in the basket chair in the kitchen, the one whose comfort makes a long business of the taking off of muddy leggings and boots. I said, 'Prince has been in a cart – he has carted muck all the afternoon.'

My wife at the stove turned round. 'Prince – oh, well done!' The children came in at that moment: 'Children, Prince has been pulling a cart!'

They clapped their hands. 'Then Prince is a real horse at last,' Sylvia added. 'So poor Kitty won't have to do all the work any more.' We all beamed with pleasure.

ADRIAN BELL, *COUNTRYSIDE CHARACTER*, 1946

Lowes Dalbiac Luard, Painter of Heavy Horses

It seems strange how few artists who lived in the heyday of the great horses made a real study of them. Perhaps it was because these horses were so common that no one thought them worth recording. Perhaps it was that the artists liked stationary models and the heavy horses were always too busy to be posed. Or perhaps they were simply regarded as lacking in the sophistication that turned a picture into a sellable article. Whatever the reason, with very few exceptions, heavy horses were mostly just part of a landscape or character in a farmyard scene. They were seldom a subject on their own.

One exception to this was Lowes Dalbiac Luard (1872–1944). He loved to draw moving models and made horses in general, and heavy horses in particular, his lifelong study.

Luard was born in India, educated at Clifton College, Bristol, and studied art at the Slade under Professors Frederick Brown and Henry Tonks. He was never stimulated by the posed model. It was only when the model moved naturally and freely that he began to draw with real interest.

In 1904, when the painter was thirty-two, he found the perfect models for

Demolition, by Lowes Dalbiac Luard (1872–1944). Oil on canvas.

204

his enthusiasms and abilities. He had moved to Paris and was entranced by the Percherons working in the streets and on the quays of the Seine. He was fascinated by the muscular make-up of the great animals and their movement and balance as they shifted huge loads of stone or sand. In all weathers and with untiring concentration, he observed these magnificent horses from the banks of the Seine. Sometimes he sketched them there as they worked and sometimes he took home an image in his remarkable photographic mind, to put it on canvas or paper in the peace of his studio.

In his later years, Luard returned to England and spent the summers at Newmarket where he drew and painted race horses, both on the gallops and on the course itself. He became fascinated by the circus, and, through his friendship with Bertram Mills, was able to go to Olympia daily to watch and record the artistes and animals performing. But his great love was still the heavy, working horse.

For those of us who love these big horses, Luard has left a wonderful legacy. An exhibition of his work recently, in the Parkin Gallery, London, showed the versatility of the artist and his dedication to his subjects. Horses standing. Horses walking. Horses pulling. Now and again, perhaps, one does wonder if, in the effort to convey movement, accurate anatomy is forgotten. But Luard's careful attention to the important lines of power and motion is unquestionable. As far as media goes, he seemed equally at home with oil on canvas, pastel on coloured board or pen and ink. In one or two simple line sketches, he conveyed the feelings of beauty, power, movement and even willingness of the horses as clearly as in the carefully planned oils.

In some drawings, effect is achieved by careful attention to the minutest detail of animal or harness, while in others precision is easily missing to emphasise main lines of motion or muscle. Certainly he was one of the few painters who understood completely the delicate mechanics of great power.

AUDREY HART, *HEAVY HORSE & DRIVING*, 1977

A Vet's View

John jumped to his feet. 'We'll have to walk down to t'river; 'osses are down there.' He left the house almost at a trot.

I eased my box of instruments from the car boot. It was a funny thing but whenever I had heavy equipment to lug about, my patients were always a long way away. This box seemed to be filled with lead and it wasn't going to get any lighter on the journey down through the walled pastures.

The old man seized a pitch fork, stabbed it into a bale of hay and hoisted it effortlessly over his shoulder. He set off again at the same brisk pace. We made our way down from one gateway to another, often walking diagonally across the fields. John didn't reduce speed and I stumbled after him, puffing a little and trying to put away the thought that he was at least fifty years older than me.

About half way down we came across a group of men at the age-old task of 'walling' – repairing a gap in one of the dry stone walls which trace their patterns everywhere on the green slopes of the Dales. One of the men looked up. 'Nice mornin', Mr Skipton,' he sang out cheerfully.

'Bugger t'mornin'. Get on wi' some work,' grunted old John in reply and the man smiled contentedly as though he had received a compliment.

I was glad when we reached the flat land at the bottom. My arms seemed to have been stretched by several inches and I could feel a trickle of sweat on my brow. Old John appeared unaffected; he flicked the fork from his shoulder and the bale thudded on to the grass.

The two horses turned towards us at the sound. They were standing fetlock deep in the pebbly shallows just beyond a little beach which merged into the green carpet of turf; nose to tail, they had been rubbing their chins gently along each other's backs, unconscious of our approach. A high cliff overhanging the far bank made a perfect wind break while on either side of us clumps of oak and beech blazed in the autumn sunshine.

'They're in a nice spot, Mr Skipton,' I said.

'Aye, they can keep cool in the hot weather and they've got the barn when winter comes.' John pointed to a low, thick-walled building with a single door. 'They can come and go as they please.'

The sound of his voice brought the horses out of the river at a stiff trot and as they came near you could see they really were old. The mare was a chestnut and the gelding was a light bay but their coats were so flecked with grey that they almost looked like roans. This was most pronounced on their faces where the sprinkling of white hairs, the sunken eyes and the deep cavity above the eyes gave them a truly venerable appearance.

For all that, they capered around John with a fair attempt at skittishness, stamping their feet, throwing their heads about, pushing his cap over his eyes with their muzzles.

'Get by, leave off!' he shouted. 'Daft awd beggars.' But he tugged absently at the mare's forelock and ran his hand briefly along the neck of the gelding.

'When did they last do any work?' I asked.

'Oh, about twelve years ago, I reckon.'

I stared at John. 'Twelve years! And have they been down here all that time?'

'Aye, just lakin' about down here, retired like. They've earned it an' all.' For a few moments he stood silent, shoulders hunched, hands deep in the pockets of his coat, then he spoke quietly as if to himself. 'They were two slaves when I was a slave.' He turned and looked at me and for a revealing moment I read in the pale blue eyes something of the agony and struggle he had shared with the animals.

'But twelve years! How old are they, anyway?'

John's mouth twisted up at one corner. 'Well you're t'vet. You tell me.'

I stepped forward confidently, my mind buzzing with Galvayne's groove, shape of marks, degree of slope and the rest; I grasped the unprotesting upper lip of the mare and looked at her teeth.

'Good God!' I gasped, 'I've never seen anything like this.' The incisors were immensely long and projecting forward till they met at an angle of about forty-five degrees. There were no marks at all – they had long since gone.

I laughed and turned back to the old man. 'It's no good, I'd only be guessing. You'll have to tell me.'

'Well she's about thirty and gelding's a year or two younger. She's had fifteen grand foals and never ailed owt except a bit of teeth trouble. We've had them rasped a time or two and it's time they were done again, I reckon. They're both losing ground and dropping bits of half chewed hay from their mouths. Gelding's the worst – has a right job champin' his grub.'

I put my hand into the mare's mouth, grasped her tongue and pulled it out to one side. A quick exploration of the molars with my other hand revealed what I suspected; the outside edges of the upper teeth were overgrown and jagged and were irritating the cheeks while the inside edges of the lower molars were in a similar state and were slightly excoriating the tongue.

'I'll soon make her more comfortable, Mr Skipton. With those sharp edges rubbed off she'll be as good as new.' I got the rasp out of my vast box, held the tongue in one hand and worked the rough surface along the teeth, checking occasionally with my fingers till the points had been sufficiently reduced.

'That's about right,' I said after a few minutes. 'I don't want to make them too smooth or she won't be able to grind her food.'

John grunted. 'Good enough. Now have a look at t'other. There's summat far wrong with him.'

I had a feel at the gelding's teeth. 'Just the same as the mare. Soon put him right, too.'

But pushing at the rasp, I had an uncomfortable feeling that something was not quite right. The thing wouldn't go fully to the back of the mouth; something was stopping it. I stopped rasping and explored again, reaching with my fingers as far as I could. And I came upon something very strange, something which shouldn't have been there at all. It was like a great chunk of bone projecting down from the roof of the mouth.

It was time I had a proper look. I got out my pocket torch and shone it over the back of the tongue. It was easy to see the trouble now; the last upper molar

207

was overlapping the lower one resulting in a gross overgrowth of the posterior border. The result was a sabre-like barb about three inches long stabbing down into the tender tissue of the gum.

That would have to come off – right now. My jauntiness vanished and I suppressed a shudder; it meant using the horrible shears – those great long-handled things with the screw operated by a cross bar. They gave me the willies because I am one of those people who can't bear to watch anybody blowing up a balloon and this was the same sort of thing only worse. You fastened the sharp blades of the shears on to the tooth and began to turn the bar slowly, slowly. Soon the tooth began to groan and creak under the tremendous leverage and you knew that any second it would break off and when it did it was like somebody letting off a rifle in your ear. That was when all hell usually broke loose but mercifully this was a quiet old horse and I wouldn't expect him to start dancing around on his hind legs. There was no pain for the horse because the overgrown part had no nerve supply – it was the noise that caused the trouble.

Returning to my crate I produced the dreadful instrument and with it a Haussman's gag which I inserted on the incisors and opened on its ratchet till the mouth gaped wide. Everything was easy to see then and of course, there it was – a great prong at the other side of the mouth exactly like the first. Great, great, now I had two to chop off.

The old horse stood patiently, eyes almost closed, as though he had seen it all and nothing in the world was going to bother him. I went through the motions with my toes curling and when the sharp crack came, the white-bordered eyes opened wide, but only in mild surprise. He never even moved. When I did the other side he paid no attention at all; in fact, with the gag prising his jaws apart he looked exactly as though he was yawning with boredom.

As I bundled the tools away, John picked up the bony spicules from the grass and studied them with interest. 'Well, poor awd beggar. Good job I got you along, young man. Reckon he'll feel a lot better now.'

On the way back, old John, relieved of his bale, was able to go twice as fast and he stumped his way up the hill at a furious pace, using the fork as a staff. I panted along in the rear, changing the box from hand to hand every few minutes.

About half way up, the thing slipped out of my grasp and it gave me a chance to stop for a breather. As the old man muttered impatiently I looked back and could just see the two horses; they had returned to the shallows and were playing together, chasing each other jerkily, their feet splashing in the water. The cliff made a dark backcloth to the picture – the shining river, the trees glowing bronze and gold and the sweet green of the grass.

Back in the farm yard, John paused awkwardly. He nodded once or twice, said 'Thank ye, young man,' then turned abruptly and walked away.

I was dumping the box thankfully into the boot when I saw the man who had spoken to us on the way down. He was sitting, cheerful as ever, in a sunny corner, back against a pile of sacks, pulling his dinner packet from an old army satchel. ·

'You've been down to see t'pensioners, then? By gaw, awd John should know the way.'

'Regular visitor, is he?'

'Regular? Every day God sends you'll see t'awd feller ploddin' down there. Rain, snow or blow, never misses. And allus has summat with him – bag o' corn, straw for their bedding.'

'And he's done that for twelve years?'

The man unscrewed his thermos flask and poured himself a cup of black tea. 'Aye, them 'osses haven't done a stroke o' work all that time and he could've got good money for them from the horse flesh merchants. Rum 'un, isn't it?'

'You're right,' I said, 'it is a rum 'un.'

Just how rum it was occupied my thoughts on the way back to the surgery. I went back to my conversation with Siegfried that morning; we had just about decided that the man with a lot of animals couldn't be expected to feel affection for individuals among them. But those buildings back there were full of John Skipton's animals – he must have hundreds.

Yet what made him trail down that hillside every day in all weathers? Why had he filled the last years of those two old horses with peace and beauty? Why had he given them a final ease and comfort which he had withheld from himself?

It could only be love.

JAMES HERRIOT, *IT SHOULDN'T HAPPEN TO A VET*, 1972

This Time Remembered

My boots into the snow
sound like a cart-horse munching oats;
    wall-led, I see shallow
      stalls in a Suffolk stable, lights
in the Borstal yard
before the siren-
        wail sends townsick boys out to the farm;
the beam still circling Orfordness.
      Lean, distracted heron
leaves the dyke as I pass . . .

MICHAEL F. FINCH, *WESTMORLAND POEMS*, 1990

The dark outlines of the famous collection of clipped yews at Painswick churchyard, Gloucestershire, contrast with the light grey Shires. (Nicholas Redman, Archivist, Whitbread plc)

The Manor Farm

The church and yew
And farmhouse slept in a Sunday silentness.
The air raised not a straw. The steep farm roof,
With tiles duskily glowing, entertained
The mid-day sun; and up and down the roof
White pigeons nestled. There was no sound but one.
Three cart-horses were looking over a gate
Drowsily through their forelocks, swishing their
    tails
Against a fly, a solitary fly.

EDWARD THOMAS, 1928

Acknowledgements
and Sources

Special thanks are due to Keith Chivers, Terry Keegan, and the late John Porter, who would have so relished this project. Diana Zeuner, editor of *Heavy Horse World*, and Patrick Walker of Watmoughs Ltd, allowed me to dip deeply into their publications. To Roger Smith of Farming Press and Charles Brook of Hutton Press a particular thank you. They have encouraged former horsemen and farmers to write of their experiences in the field, and continue to do so. They are tapping a huge store of information and interest, and laying a store for the future.

Much appreciated help has been received from:

Anne Butterworth, British Museum, British Percheron Horse Society, Alex Christian, Clydesdale Horse Society, Day & Sons, East of England Agricultural Society, Ex Libris, *Farmers Weekly*, Audrey Hart, Home Office, Marie Lee, National Federation of Young Farmers' Clubs, David Pratt, Rare Breeds Survival Trust, Clive Richardson, *Scottish Farmer*, Shire Horse Society, Donald J. Smith, John Stone, Suffolk Horse Society, Allan Turner, Walsall Leather Centre.

I am grateful to the authors and publishers of the following publications for permission to reproduce material:

Andrews, Malcolm, *Heavy Horse World*, 1987
Bailey, Jocelyn, *The Village Blacksmith*, Shire Publications, 1977
Baird, Eric, *The Clydesdale Horse*, B.T. Batsford Ltd, 1982
Bakewell, David, *Heavy Horse World*, 1987
Bell, Adrian, *Countryside Character*, Blandford Press, 1946
Biddell, Herman, *The Suffolk Stud Book, Vol. I*, 1880
Burrell, Sir Merrick R., *British Percheron Horse Society, Vol. I*, 1922
Charlton, A.B., *The Shire Horse Society Jubilee History*, 1928

Chivers, Keith, *The Shire Horse*, J.A. Allen & Co. Ltd, 1976

——, *Heavy Horse & Driving*, 1977

——, *Heavy Horse & Driving*, March/April 1982

——, *The London Harness Horse Parade*, 1985

——, *Heavy Horse World*, Summer 1994

Creaser, John J., *Sixty Years in the Isle*, privately published, 1990

Davis, Frank, *Country Life*, 17/24 December 1970

Day, Herbert, *My Life with Horses*, Hutton Press, 1983

Day's Everyday Farriery, 15th Issue, 1885

Drew's Select Clydesdale Stud Book, 1884

Edinburgh, HRH The Duke of, *History With A Purpose*, SHS/RASB, 1988

Evans, G.E., *The Farm and the Village*, Faber & Faber Ltd, 1969

Exley, Alan, *Heavy Horse & Driving*, Spring 1977

Finch, Michael F., *Westmorland Poems*, Titus Wilson, 1990

Fream, W., *Elements of Agriculture*, John Murray (Publishers) Ltd, 1949

Freud, C., *The Times*, 8 October 1993

Frost, J. Albert, *The Shire Horse in Peace and War*, Vinton & Co. Ltd, 1915

Gifford, Angela, *Heavy Horse World*, 1988

Gillespie, Duncan, *The Scottish Farmer*, 1986

——, *Heavy Horse World*, 1988

Hall, Alfred, *Ploughman's Progress*, Farming Press Books, Ipswich, 1992

Hart, Audrey, *Carriage Driving*, 1988

Hart, Edward, *Golden Guinea Book of Heavy Horses Past and Present*, David & Charles Publishers, Newton Abbot, 1976

——, *Heavy Horse & Driving*, 1977

——, *Shire Horses*, B.T. Batsford Ltd, 1983

——, *Yorkshire Life*, December 1983

——, *The Book of the Heavy Horse*, Patrick Stephens Ltd, Yeovil, 1986

——, *Heavy Horse World*, October 1988

——, *The Ark*, Rare Breeds Survival Trust, March 1992

——, *Heavy Horse World*, 1994

Hart, Frank, *Country Life*, 1934

Heiney, Paul, *The Times*, 18 June 1994

Hennell, T., *Change in the Farm*, Cambridge University Press, Cambridge, 1934

Herriot, James, *It Shouldn't Happen to a Vet*, Michael Joseph Ltd, 1972

Holden, Bryan, *The Long Haul*, J.A. Allen & Co. Ltd, 1985

Holden, Marion, *The Field Year Book*, David & Charles Publishers, Newton Abbot, 1972

Jenkins, J. Geraint, *Agricultural Transport in Wales*, National Museum of Wales, 1962

Jones, Llewelyn, *Schoolin's Log*, Michael Joseph Ltd, 1980

Keegan, Terry, *The Heavy Horse: Its Harness and Harness Decorations*, Pelham Books, 1973

——, *Horse Brasses and Decorations*, Walsall Leather Centre, 1990

King, C., *Heavy Horse World*, 1992

Lydekker, R., *Guide to the Specimens of the Horse Family (Equidae)*, British Museum, 1922

McGregor, Hugh, *The Scottish Farmer*, 1 January 1955

——, *The Scottish Farmer*, 1 January 1959

McWhirter, Norris, *The Guinness Book of Records*, 1994

Main, J., *Young Farmer's Manual*, James Ridgway, 1847

Messum, David, *The Life and Works of Lucy Kemp-Welch*, Antique Collectors' Club, Woodbridge, 1976

Neale, K.J., *The 'Colony' Suffolks*, Home Office, 1975

Nixon, David, *Pictures on a Wall*, privately published, 1983

——, *The Song of the Chilterns*, privately published, 1978

Oaksey, John, *Pride of the Shires*, Hutchinson,1980

Ottley, Reginald, L., *The Listener*, June 1960

Pawson, H. Cecil, *Robert Blakewell*, Crosby Lockwood & Son Ltd, 1957

Pearce, J.B., *Heavy Horse & Driving*, Spring 1977

Pollard, Henry, privately published, 1984

Porter, John M., *Heavy Horse & Driving*, Spring 1977

——, *Heavy Horse & Driving*, Summer 1977

Reffold, Harry, *Pie for Breakfast*, Hutton Press, 1984

Richardson, Robert C., *Some Fell on Stony Ground*, Geo. R. Reeve Ltd, 1978

Sewell, Anna, *Black Beauty*, Jarrold & Sons Ltd, Norwich, 1877

Sidney, Samuel, *The Book of the Horse*, 1880s

Standard Cyclopedia of Modern Agriculture, Gresham Books Ltd, Henley-on-Thames, 1910

Sturt, George, *The Wheelright's Shop*, Cambridge University Press, Cambridge, 1923

The Suffolk Stud Book, Vol. I, 1880

Thomas, Edward, *Collected Poems*, Faber & Faber Ltd, 1928

Tunnicliffe, C.F., *My Country Book*, The Studio, 1942

Tusser, Thomas, *Five Hundred Points of Good Husbandry*, 1524–80

Twist, Michael F., *The Spacious Days*, Farming Press Books, Ipswich, 1992

Walters, W.T., *The Percheron Horse*, privately published, 1886

Warren, C. Henry, *Corn Country*, B.T. Batsford Ltd, 1940
Weatherley, Lee, *The Field*, 20 June 1974
——, *Heavy Horse & Driving*, Spring 1977
——, *Great Horses of Britain*, Saiga, 1978
Whitlock, Ralph, *Gentle Giants*, Lutterworth Press, 1976
Willson, W.H., *British Percheron Horse Society, Vol. I*, 1922
Wright, Charlie, *Farm Horses*, Young Farmers Publication, 1950
Wright, Revd Philip, *Rustic Rhymes*, privately published, 1985